For better or worse, the Affordable Care Act transformed U.S. healthcare. After the 2016 election, President Donald Trump and the Republican majorities in Congress plan a new direction for America. What will it mean for America? For healthcare? For you?

DO NOT READ THIS BOOK UNLESS YOU WANT TO KNOW THE ANSWERS.

Nelson, Harry, and Fuller, Rob
From ObamaCare to TrumpCare: Why You Should Care ISBN: 978-0-692-82390-3, 978-0-692-82389-7

First Edition
Printed in the United States of America

Published By RX4 Group
11835 W Olympic Blvd, Suite 900 Los Angeles, California 90064
www.rx4group.com

While the authors have made every effort to publish accurate Internet addresses and other data at the time of the publication, neither the publisher nor the authors assume any responsibility for errors, or for changes that occur after publication. Further, the publisher and authors do not assume any responsibility for third part websites or their content.

Disclaimer: The material in this publication is intended as general commentary only, and neither purports nor intends to be advice to be relied upon. Readers should not act on the basis of prediction or any matter in this publication without considering (and if appropriate taking) professional advice with due regard to their own particular circumstances. The authors and publisher expressly disclaim all an any liability to any person, whether purchase of the publication or not, in respect of anything and the consequences of anything done or omitted to be done by any reader or listener to this book.

FROM OBAMACARE TO TRUMPCARE: WHY YOU SHOULD CARE

This book is dedicated to the people who suffer because U.S. healthcare is broken and to the dedicated professionals who work tirelessly to keep people alive and healthy in a challenging system.

"Before I go on with this short history, let me make a general observation – the test of a first-rate intelligence is the ability to hold two opposed ideas in the mind at the same time, and still retain the ability to function. One should, for example, be able to see that things are hopeless and yet be determined to make them otherwise."

F. Scott Fitzgerald, The Crack-Up

TABLE OF CONTENTS

Foreword

For anyone trying to understand the challenges and opportunities in the U.S. healthcare marketplace, the election of Donald Trump adds a new wrinkle to an already complicated picture.

Over the past six years, the American healthcare industry has undergone a systemic change and massive realignment. Much (though not all) of the transformation to date has been driven by the enactment of the Affordable Care Act (ACA), better known as ObamaCare, which for the first time offered health insurance options to people who would otherwise be bankrupted by healthcare costs, or simply didn't have jobs that provided insurance. In many states, Medicaid expansion opened up an option that translated to economic security. For other Americans, the ACA was a disappointment or worse: an expense without improvement in their quality of life.

President Trump has promised to repeal and replace or, at a minimum, roll back the ACA. Some Americans, both patients and industry insiders, are terrified. Others are elated. What will this mean for patients, for healthcare providers, and for other stakeholders in the U.S. healthcare system?

As healthcare regulatory lawyers, we've spent the last six years since the 2010 enactment of the ACA explaining the mechanics of the law and its various components. We do our best to clarify a confusing array of laws and regulations and guide our clients - hospitals, physician groups, behavioral health and post-acute facilities, labs, pharmacies, digital health, and life science companies - in strategizing how to navigate these waters.

A few months before the November 2016 election, our

friend Larry Cohen, CEO of Glyphix, suggested that people wanted to know our predictions for what was going to happen with U.S. healthcare after the election. In Southern California, where we're based, the conventional wisdom was that Hillary Clinton was a lock. So we wrote a piece entitled "The Election's Over, Now What for Healthcare" trying to anticipate the Clinton healthcare agenda. Although Clinton and Obama were relatively aligned, there were big questions about how Hillary would respond to challenges (like the languishing state insurance exchanges) and whether she would advance more progressive changes (like pricing controls on Big Pharma or rescheduling marijuana).

Late on the evening of November 8, we realized that this decision was what our kids would call an "epic fail" and that a rewrite was in order. The next chapter in American healthcare was going to look very different.

We quickly scrambled to rewrite and circulate our thoughts. The piece went viral, leading to a deluge of questions, requests for speeches and media interviews, and the suggestion that we expand our thoughts into this book. As we reached out to healthcare industry leaders, our sense was that everyone was in a state of confusion. The interest came not only from our regular audience of healthcare providers and industry insiders, but also from our friends and colleagues who are anxious about what the future portends for them and their families.

We considered that there was some danger in predicting events that are almost at hand, but decided that there are too many people confused about what's going to happen, what's going to change, and what people should do about it. We decided to dive in and embarked on an ambitious publishing schedule.

Our goal is to slice through the overheated rhetoric on both sides and offer an assessment that is as apolitical as possible about where U.S. healthcare has been and where it is heading. The Affordable Care Act simultaneously deserves to be praised for its efforts to close the gaps in our healthcare system, and criticized for a messy implementation that failed to control spiraling costs. It contained a series of policy choices, just as TrumpCare will, which address complex, multifaceted problems on the ground. We've done our job if advocates for (and detractors of) ObamaCare and TrumpCare both find things to be unhappy about in our analysis.

> *The Affordable Care Act simultaneously deserves to be praised for its efforts to close the gaps in our healthcare system, and criticized for a messy implementation that failed to control spiraling costs.*

While opponents will naturally take issue with the other side's choices, we believe it is possible to be reasonably objective and, where appropriate, both appreciative and critical of the competing visions. This book puts together many of the strands of speeches and articles we've written with this goal in mind.

We're not prophets, but we have looked at both the ACA and its alternatives enough to feel like we can contribute something to the dialogue. As lawyers, we've advised clients on both sides of the political divide, as well as countless others just trying to keep their heads down and navigate confusing waters. Similarly, as investors, we have tried to tease out the bright spots and opportunities.

We've tried to write this book as a useful post-mortem on the ACA, an assessment of the expected Trump alternative, and some broader thoughts about where we go from here. Although our work focuses on advising healthcare providers, we've included thoughts for patients, because, as patients, we are all affected by the changes that have brought our system into its current form and the changes still ahead. Our goal is not to be political, but instead to think critically and carefully about where we've been and where we're headed.

We hope that readers of this book come away with some clarity over the big questions ahead for U.S. healthcare. While we have the best healthcare that exists in some respects, we have a long way to go in others. There are more chapters unfolding in the months ahead, and we look forward to revisiting them and getting your feedback.

Acknowledgments

We owe a debt of gratitude to a phenomenal team of editors whose willingness to jump in and dedicated teamwork made this book happen in a very short period of time. Reva Nelson astutely managed this project with aplomb. Andrew Bird and Rena Selya worked tirelessly and brought valuable insights in their editing and revisions. This book would not have come together as it did without the work of this group.

Larry Cohen, Brad Wilder, and the rest of the team at Glyphix, have been incredible on so many projects that we sometimes take them for granted. They took us seriously when we presented a ridiculous schedule and dove into the work of translating our messy ideas into something clear and compelling.

We are blessed to have partners and colleagues at Nelson

Hardiman who support the chances we take, even when they go beyond the traditional scope of what lawyers and law firms typically do. We are grateful to be surrounded by a people who believe in us and support us, even when we suggest doing things beyond the realm of imagination.

How This Book Is Organized
This is organized into 10 chapters, followed by an appendix.

Chapter 1, "Setting the Scene: The Brokenness of U.S. Healthcare" presents an overview of the problem(s) of the U.S. healthcare system, including high cost for relative low quality (compared to other developed countries) and lack of access to care. Chapter 1 also explains the piecemeal historical development of healthcare coverage in America as an outgrowth of private employer-based insurance coverage with the 1965 infill of the Medicare program for the elderly and the Medicaid program for the poor. The differences between the two programs set the stage for many of the conflicts that remain at the heart of the political conflict 50 years later.

Chapter 2, "The Strange, Wonkish Road to ObamaCare," sketches the history of U.S. healthcare reform from the early 1970s, when the model that would ultimately become ObamaCare first emerged, to the ultimate 2010 enactment of the Affordable Care Act (ACA). Over four decades, the U.S. enacted addressed minor issues until the Obama administration signed into the law the most comprehensive healthcare reform law since the establishment of Medicare and Medicaid.

Chapter 3, "The Good, Bad, and Ugly of ObamaCare Implementation," examines the roll-out of ObamaCare, the impact of the political conflict and Supreme Court decisions, and the signature achievements, failures, and conflicts that ensued from 2010 through the 2016 election of President Donald Trump on the promise of ACA repeal.

Chapter 4, "A Better Way? The Republican Plan for U.S. Healthcare," explores the Republican vision of what would replace ObamaCare developed under the leadership of House Speaker Paul Ryan and the nominee for Secretary of the Department of Health and Human Services, Tom Price, and offers an assessment of Republican plans.

Chapter 5, "The Trump Wild Card," considers the personal approach of President Trump to U.S. healthcare, assessing the questions of where Trump appears to be at odds with Republican plans and how potential conflicts over healthcare between Speaker Ryan and President Trump may play out in the coming four or eight years.

Chapter 6, "Envisioning TrumpCare" offers predictions for how the Trump administration and Congress are likely to tackle healthcare, including what comes after the threatened repeal of the Affordable Care Act and the changes ahead.

Chapter 7, "This is Real: Implications for Patients," examines how new "TrumpCare" healthcare policies are likely to affect patients of all ages and incomes.

Chapter 8, "Unprepared? Implications for the Healthcare Industry," evaluates the impact of legislative changes on the different segments of the healthcare provider community, offering an assessment of which sectors of the healthcare industry are likely to be winners and losers with TrumpCare.

Chapter 9, "How TrumpCare Intersects with Broader Forces of Healthcare Transformation," explores the extent to which the legislative shifts are muted by broader economic, behavioral, and technological changes and tries to predict how the other structural forces of transformation are likely to align with TrumpCare.

Chapter 10, "Big Questions Ahead: Where Do We Go From Here?" examines the longer term challenges ahead in attempting to fix U.S. healthcare, and offers some thoughts about where the long-term solutions may be found.

In the Appendix, we've included some additional resources, including a glossary of terms and a summary for anyone wanting the "Cliff Notes" version of our concepts as a refresher, cocktail party talking points, or an alternative way to digest this book.

A Note About the Terms "ObamaCare" and "TrumpCare"
HillaryCare. RomneyCare. BernieCare. Are these terms just lazy shorthand formulations to save us the trouble of writing or saying the whole mouthful of "the health reform plan promoted by Hillary Clinton/Mitt Romney/Bernie Sanders"? Are they intended by political opponents to be derisive and mocking? Exactly when did every politician's plan for healthcare come to be known as Your-Name-Here-Care?

It's not clear who started this trend, but ObamaCare certainly seems to have taken the whole "-Care" phenomenon to a new level. The media liked it because it was easier to say when reporting on the enactment or the Supreme Court battles. It was much easier than the original clumsy name of the "Patient Protection and Affordable Care Act," ("Pee-pack-ah") as the 2010 law was originally known before being shortened to the Affordable Care Act. For Republicans, "ObamaCare" offered an easy handle to criticize the new law (and implicitly compare it to the 1993 failed version of HillaryCare). Like other put-downs, Democrats re-appropriated it as a badge of pride, as in the protesters at the Supreme Court holding up "Hands Off My ObamaCare" signs. Eventually, even President Obama claimed the term.

TrumpCare, meanwhile is a newer formulation. It doesn't yet roll off the tongue like ObamaCare, but just wait. After all, it offers a convenient shorthand for whatever the Republican plan that replaces ObamaCare comes to be called. We haven't heard the President-elect use the term, as President Obama adopted ObamaCare, but given his penchant for using his name as a brand, we suspect it's just a matter of time.

Throughout this book, we use the terms neutrally: not as insults or praise, but as convenient "code" for the sets of laws, regulations, and policies through which the recent healthcare reform of 2010-2016 occurred (ObamaCare) and the expected healthcare reform 2017 through either 2021 or 2025 (TrumpCare). While we are not shy about expressing our misgivings about either where we've been or where we're headed, our goal is hard-headed realism and not advocacy or opposition to one or the other.

FROM OBAMACARE TO TRUMPCARE: WHY YOU SHOULD CARE

HARRY NELSON & ROB FULLER

ONE:
SETTING THE SCENE: THE BROKENNESS OF U.S. HEALTHCARE

Understanding the recent past, present, and future of American healthcare begins with an understanding of its systemic challenges: (1) price; (2) outcomes, (3) access; and (4) cost allocation. We start with the problems of paying high prices for mediocre outcomes. We have the distinction of spending by far the most on healthcare of any country (18% of our GDP), with relatively crummy results to show for it. The U.S. ranks poorly compared to other advanced industrialized countries as measured by life expectancy and most health outcomes – rates of chronic conditions, obesity, infant mortality – other than mortality rates for cancer. When we talk about the need for healthcare cost reduction and quality improvement, this is just a fancy way of saying we are paying too much for what we are getting.

When we talk about the need for healthcare cost reduction and quality improvement, this is just a fancy way of saying we are paying too much for what we are getting.

Beyond price and outcomes, the other systemic challenges in U.S. healthcare are access to healthcare and cost allocation (i.e., how people get care and how we pay for it). Healthcare involves a unique bundle of goods and services. It encompasses some universal, fairly predictable things that we all need (e.g., routine primary care services, like annual physicals) as well as treatment for unexpected things like catastrophic accidents and major illnesses, and the ongoing needs of people with developmental disabilities. Some healthcare needs are things we tend to think of as personal and private (such as whether a person gets treatment for pain), but other needs have public ramifications. When a person has a virus, we all benefit and are protected when the person gets treated, and we all risk getting sick if the person doesn't get needed care and we come into contact with the infected person. Healthcare also touches some fundamental ideas about justice and human dignity. Most people regard access to care as a hallmark of a compassionate society, and many people are troubled when inequality of resources extends to unequal outcomes, such as the fact that being rich translates to living longer than other people.

Because of all of these social and moral considerations, healthcare has become a much more complicated set of goods and services for us as a society to agree on and set rules of distribution. It is not simply a matter of letting people buy whatever healthcare they can afford in a pure market situation. Instead, healthcare involves difficult policy questions, such as when society will pay for other people to get care and when we will not. Most people, for example, readily agree that we should pay for expensive interventional treatment when a child is afflicted with cancer, but the decision is more difficult when we are discussing care for an elderly, lifelong smoker who develops lung cancer. What about extended end-of-life hospitalization for a person with a poor prognosis? These issues highlight very difficult, nuanced questions that are not well suited to our polarized political system. Our political process may not be ideal to address healthcare, but, as they say, it's the only one we've got. Before we take on the political solutions and the issue of how to reform our health insurance system, let's take a closer look at the problems and the state of the healthcare system that both ObamaCare and TrumpCare must navigate.

A Low Quality System at an Unparalleled Cost

The conundrum that politicians face in addressing healthcare policy is that the American healthcare *system* is unparalleled in the world, but our actual *health* lags by all important measures. Looking at the resources we devote to healthcare and our ability to produce first-class physicians, we cannot be matched. We have 4,500 of the best hospitals in the world. We have the best medical schools. We have the most innovation in medical, pharmaceutical, and biological products. We have the best emergency medicine system for a large population across a vast geographical expanse.

Yet when we compare the population's health and mortality morbidity statistics to other industrialized nations, as reflected on Table 1, we see a different reality: when it comes to overall rankings of healthcare cost, quality, and efficiency, the U.S. ranks last overall and worst in efficiency compared to other "First World" countries. As Table 1 demonstrates, when you measure U.S. healthcare against other leading advanced industrialized countries, we're doing something wrong.

Table 1

Comparing Relative Healthcare Cost, Quality, and Efficiency

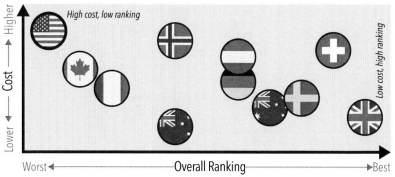

Healthcare Cost vs. Overall Ranking

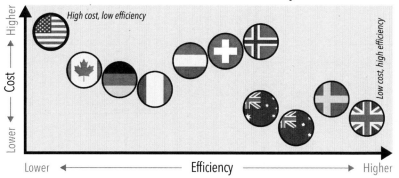

Healthcare Cost vs. Efficiency

NOTE: The studies summarized in the "Overall Ranking" chart evaluated developed countries according to their quality (effectiveness, safety, and coordination of care), infant mortality, preventable deaths, life expectancy, and access/affordability of needed care. The studies ranked efficiency according to time and expense of dealing with insurance administration, lack of communication among healthcare providers and duplicative testing.

Source: The Commonwealth Fund (citing 2007 International Health Policy Survey; 2008 International Health Policy Survey of Sicker Adults; 2009 International Health Policy Survey of Primary Care Physicians; Commonwealth Fund Commission on a High Performance Health System National Scorecard; and OECD Health Data, 2009).

It's not a matter of investment, because, as Table 2 reflects, we are actually spending significantly more per capita than any other country in the world, including all of the countries with better healthcare systems than ours.

Table 2

U.S. Health Spending vs. Rest of the World

Total health expenditure per capita, public and private, 2010 (or nearest year)

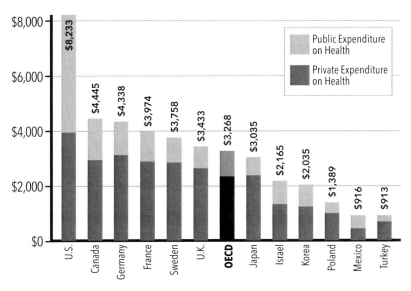

Source: OECD Health Data 2012

How did the United States end up with the most expensive but lowest quality health system in the advanced industrialized world? The cause is straightforward and well-known to clinicians, but it is not what any politician wants to hear. It comes down to people's behavior, summarized by the six S's: sugar, salt, smoking, sedentariness, stress, and senior (i.e., end-of-life) choices.

The problem is that, in order for politicians to advocate improvements to our collective health, they would need to point their fingers at the American people. Neither

Democrats nor Republicans have shown a willingness to earn the unpopularity that addressing this dirty little secret would entail. The biggest challenge of U.S. healthcare is that each "S" causes a significant public health issue that cannot be solved by insurance programs, access to healthcare resources or more or less governmental intervention in the healthcare industry.

If you aren't sure you believe the country-by-country rankings on Table 1, let's take a look at some salient data points. A better healthcare system would presumably keep its citizens living longer and enjoying good health for more of their lives, right?

Table 3

Life Expectancy at Birth by Country

Country	Life Expectancy
Japan	83.4
Spain	83.2
Australia	82.2
Israel	82.1
Korea	81.8
United Kingdom	81.1
Portugal	80.8
United States	**78.8**
China	75.4
Russia	70.7

Source: Organization for Economic Cooperation and Development, 2013

As Table 3 highlights, when you compare the U.S. to other leading developed countries, we are living shorter, less healthy lives. In fact, Americans have shorter life spans than roughly 40 other countries. (When you adjust for healthy life expectancy, taking account of only years that people actually live in good health, the United States climbs slightly higher but are still behind roughly 25 countries.) Americans live, on average, five years less than Singaporeans and three years less than Australians. The primary reasons are lifestyle-driven disease, such as lung cancer from tobacco use and high coronary heart disease rates. We eat too much sugar, leading to Type 2 (adult onset) diabetes, and too much salt, leading to hypertension. The diabetes numbers are staggering: roughly 13% of adults have diabetes and another roughly 37% who are prediabetic (i.e., in a gray area between normal blood sugar levels and a diagnosis of diabetes). You don't have to be a mathematician to add those two numbers and calculate that half of the U.S. population has a serious health issue. Roughly two-thirds of U.S. adults have a related problem with obesity. To use Britain as a comparison, estimates of diabetes are less than half of U.S. levels.

This same comparison to other developed countries can be made for many other progressive diseases. These statistics should be setting off alarm bells about diet, exercise, and stress management changes that Americans need to make to improve U.S. healthcare outcomes. While "wellness" is certainly a growing priority, politicians are surprisingly quiet about where the real effort of closing the health gap with the rest of the developed world lies.

A similar gap appears when you compare disease rates of

Americans socioeconomically. To stick with the example of diabetes, a 2013 Illinois Department of Public Health Study found that the rate of diabetes was 5.5% for college graduates, compared to 14.6% for people who did not graduate high school – nearly 2.5 times higher for less educated people.[1] Analyzed by income, the rate of diabetes was 6.0% for people earning more than $75,000 annually, compared with 12.7% for people earning less than $15,000 annually.

Table 4

Diseases by Income Level

White, non-Hispanics, age 55-64

Source: J. of the Am. Medical Assn., 2006: 295 [17]: 2037-2045

In another study (reflected in Table 4), the disease rates for diabetes, hypertension, heart attacks, and lung disease – some of the most common problematic health conditions – were higher for Americans than Britons, and higher in both countries the less you earned.

The data trends across all of these diseases are consistent with the findings in Table 1 that Britons get better healthcare than Americans, but also that health outcomes are have a socioeconomic dimension. People with the highest income do the best, and people with the lowest income do the worst when it comes to health outcomes.

While it may not be a surprise that higher income affords advantages that extend to greater flexibility and power to make good health choices, these data points make it difficult to deny the reality of healthcare inequality within the U.S. The pattern repeats across all of the chronic medical conditions that drive up U.S. healthcare costs and make it the most expensive system in the world

What is challenging about these chronic, behaviorally-rooted problems is that the opportunity to improve health outcomes and reduce cost is not about spending money on lab testing, doctor visits, and more healthcare services - the things we think of as normal healthcare delivery. It isn't that providing doctor visits doesn't help at all, but rather that more and better clinical healthcare delivery is only going to address about 20% of the gap.

Table 5
How Does the U.S. Close the Health Gap?

We can improve up to **20%** via better healthcare service delivery and efficiency

The other **80%** will not improve without better housing, education, diet, and social support for those in need.

NOTE: This applies both to closing the gap between the U.S. and other developed countries, as well as the gap across socioeconomic levels.

Source: Booske, Athens, et al, Different Perspectives For Assigning Weights to Determinants of Health, University of Wisconsin Population Health Institute (2010); see also Harry J. Heiman and Samantha Artiga, Kaiser Family Foundation, Beyond Health Care: The Role of Social Determinants in Promoting Health and Health Equity, November 4, 2015.

Table 5 highlights that as much as 80% of the health gap is only addressable through long-term social support and education to influence the American people to make better choices: reduce salt and sugar in their diet, quit smoking, get regular exercise, make intelligent end-of-life choices about quality of life and life extending interventions, and manage stress more effectively.

One challenge is that the effects of these often don't manifest until later in life. Consider Table 6, which analyzes how health spending increases over the average life span in the U.S. and other developed countries:

For the majority of people, health spending is low from

childhood into their 50s. The effects of aging and bad habits like unhealthy eating, smoking, or not exercising don't necessarily manifest until the late 50s or 60s. That's when the consequences of long-term choices manifest in heart attacks, strokes, diabetes, and the other expensive conditions that drive healthcare costs and decrease quality of life.

Table 6

Annual Per Capita Healthcare Costs by Age

Source: Dan Munro, Forbes, Dec. 30, 2012 (citing Mark Roth, Pittsburgh Post-Gazette Dec. 2009)

Stress is an often misunderstood issue and a special category. It isn't so much the psychological impact on any particular individual's psyche, it is the impact of our collective economic activity on our health. When you compare the U.S. to other industrialized nations, our average GDP per person is higher. In fact, the average economic production of the American worker is 10 times that of the average Chinese worker. In simple terms, we have opted to be the most productive economic population on the planet, and as a consequence it should not surprise us that we suffer, healthwise. We have a proportionally higher incidence of illness, sickness, injury, and disease. We put this all under the category of stress - we stress our average workers more and their average health status shows it.

The issues surrounding this phenomenon are complex. Do we need to mirror France and Germany with much shorter work weeks and double or triple average vacation away from jobs than we currently enjoy? If we value economic activity, the answer is no. If we value our health, the answer may be yes. From a statistical standpoint, the data would seem to indicate there are no "have it both ways" solutions. If you are going to stress your workforce for higher economic productivity per worker, your average worker is not going to be as healthy as workers in other, less stressed societies.

Lack of Access to Care
In addition to the high cost and relative low quality of our healthcare system, the other major problem of our system is lack of access to care, or, more precisely, mal-distribution of access to our resources. Our healthcare resources are akin to our food resources. We have plenty of food for everyone, and we have plenty of healthcare providers to meet almost all of the basic needs of the population. Yet there is a mismatch created when the cost of food or the cost of healthcare exceeds the ability of a significant portion of the population to afford it.

The problem of the lack of access to care is related to the problems of cost and quality. Lack of access to routine healthcare in a physician's office or an urgent care clinic, for example, drives many patients to delay seeking care until their symptoms have become dire. The emergency room becomes the front line of care. As a consequence, Americans score terribly on numerous measurements of proactive healthcare such as weight or tobacco and other substance use. They seek care too late in the process in the most expensive possible venue – and the only venue where the healthcare provider is required by law to treat them.

The same battles over the access problem seem to have played out on an endless loop over the past half century. Throughout that time, the tension has been between Democratic advocacy for government to improve and expand the safety net to provide healthcare (and other resources) to people in need, and Republican advocacy for a more self-determinative and market-driven process in lieu of government intervention. As we address in upcoming chapters, our goal is to understand the significant challenges that any approach, from progressive to conservative, faces.

One of the biggest challenges is that we have shifted from a conversation about what kind of healthcare Americans need to a conversation about what kind of healthcare insurance they need. Both ObamaCare, TrumpCare, and whatever comes after them face the challenges of the status quo, including a majority of Americans invested in their existing coverage and a health system driven by health insurance coverage and third-party payment, leading to distorted pricing. In the next part of Chapter 1, we examine how the key components of U.S. healthcare access have developed as a patchwork rather than a unified system over the past 75 years.

> One of the biggest challenges is that we have shifted from a conversation about what kind of healthcare Americans need to a conversation about what kind of healthcare insurance they need.

Getting To Where We Are: The Patchwork of the Status Quo

Although cost, quality, and access are the recurrent deficits that come up in discussions of our healthcare system, it is critical to understand a deeper challenge of how we got to where we are.

The U.S. approach to healthcare access over the past century has not been systematic. Instead, our system emerged as a series of "patches," each intended to fill the gaps in the system. One of the big challenges in reforming healthcare is that we are not designing from scratch, but instead are forced to layer onto a flawed existing landscape. Medicare, Medicaid, and employer-provided insurance coverage are all entrenched institutions, with their own constituencies, that will not readily agree to any meaningful change.

> One of the big challenges in reforming healthcare is that we are not designing from scratch, but instead are forced to layer onto a flawed existing landscape.

Employer-Based Healthcare Coverage

In the first half of the 20th century, the model of employer-based coverage went from the exception to the rule. As we shifted from a rural to an increasingly urban workforce, employers provided healthcare insurance as a benefit of employment. At the present time, an estimated 175 million Americans are covered by employer plans. Before the rise of employment-based health insurance, wealthy people mostly paid out-of-pocket for care in elite settings and the poor got their care in charitable or public settings. Religious and ethnic institutions were created to provide care to their own, and many of our contemporary healthcare systems had their roots in Christian and Jewish religious organizations of the early twentieth century. There were numerous attempts before and after World War II to implement some type of national health insurance coverage in order to protect citizens and provide physicians with financial stability, but these plans ran into fierce resistance from physicians and the pharmaceutical industry, among other interest groups. During the Cold War, national health insurance was characterized as "socialized medicine" and was therefore politically and ideologically suspect.

In the post-World War II era, employer-based insurance coverage became the predominant source of healthcare access. Although we speak more commonly of college education and the ability to buy a home as the universal middle-class "American Dream" that emerged after World War II, healthcare insurance coverage was embedded in the package as part of what employers were expected to provide. Unions, for example, negotiated for healthcare along with retirement benefits as part of the compensation that employees earned through their labor. Coverage varied between plans to cover primary and specialty medical care, as well as particular healthcare services, such as dental, vision, hearing, and later, substance abuse.

The problem with this approach was that it excluded several large chunks of the U.S. population, most notably the elderly (who worked in a period before retirement benefits were part of the deal) and the poor (both those who were unemployed and those employed in work that didn't provide healthcare coverage). As we'll explore below, the decisions to isolate the two systems for the elderly and the poor from each other has been a fateful one for the ongoing story of U.S. healthcare.

Medicare and Medicaid

The huge gaps of healthcare for the oldest and poorest Americans were both addressed comprehensively a half-century ago by the biggest legislated healthcare reform in American history prior to the ACA, the enactment of Medicaid and Medicare. The contrast between the way that the two programs developed is not only fascinating, but gets to the heart of the ongoing conflict that divides America.

President Lyndon Johnson signed them both into law in 1965 as part of the Great Society initiatives. Both grew out of growing public attention in the 1960s to the limitations of an employer-based system in providing access to care, and the fact that the largest uninsured segments of the U.S. population were the elderly and the poor. What distinguished the two programs was their focus on clearly defined populations: Medicare for the elderly and Medicaid for the poor.

Both programs generated political and popular reactions, echoes of which still reverberate five decades later. Medicare, which provided federally funded health coverage for anyone over the age of 65, was relatively popular from its inception. Americans embraced the idea of a government program to ensure healthcare access for the elderly. Whether it was compassion for a generation that had lived through World War I, the Great Depression, and World War II, or the fact that everyone could relate to getting old and the importance of dignity and respect for the elderly, Medicare was popular. It may not have hurt was that it was also initially a short-term benefit, given that the average American man had a life expectancy of between 65 and 70 in 1965. In the year after its enactment, nearly 20 million Americans signed up, representing over 90% of those eligible.

Medicaid, on the other hand, was not universally embraced. Whether because of a contrast in shared experience (we all get old, but not all of us experience poverty), negative moral judgment about people who do not break out of poverty, or the lifetime cost of caring for the poor (as opposed to the relatively shorter, defined window after age 65 of caring for Medicare beneficiaries), Medicaid was met by ambivalence in some places and opposition in others.

This ambivalence about Medicaid manifested in several respects. In contrast to Medicare, which from the start was entirely federally funded and administered (through the Center for Medicare and Medicaid Services (CMS), within the U.S. Department of Health and Human Services (HHS)), Medicaid required a compromise combination of mixed state and federal funding under state administration. In other words, each state had to partially fund and oversee the Medicaid program. As a consequence, each state had to make an initial decision about participating in Medicaid, a step that was absent in the Medicare program.

The fact that each state operates its own Medicaid program separately accounts for why it bears different names in different places (e.g., Medi-Cal in California and TennCare in Tennessee). The siloing of Medicare from Medicaid, as well as of each state's Medicaid program from other states, has had profound implications. As we'll examine in Chapter 3, the differences became even more profound in the past seven years as the Medicaid program gained 20 million new beneficiaries (going from roughly 50 million in 2009 to 70 million today) at the same time that many states decided, after the first Supreme Court decision upholding the ACA, not to participate in the Affordable Care Act expansion of the Medicaid program.

The current Republican antipathy to Medicaid echoes the initial reception of the Medicaid program: only 26 states initially agreed to participate in Medicaid. It took 17 years, until 1982, before all 50 states were participating.

The underlying tension and point of dispute – from 1965 until today – is the question of how narrow or expansive Medicaid coverage for the poor should be. The idea that there is a moral dimension to poverty and that poverty is a conscious choice for at least a subset of the poor runs deep in American history and culture. This idea has led to a conflict. The left make no moral assumptions about the status of being poor, and see the provision of the poor with healthcare coverage as a fundamental right and the state's moral obligation. On the right, some question whether Medicaid is the best way to provide care, but express the opposing concern that providing healthcare and other benefits to the poor creates the risk, to quote South Dakota Governor Dennis Daugaard, that "some people who can work will become more dependent on government" in the process. This fear gets to the heart of a key underlying sentiment of those who oppose entitlements like Medicaid in general – that these benefits may motivate some of the poor to forego working.

As a result of this enduring conflict, in the decades after its enactment, Medicaid had narrow groups that state programs were required to cover – children living below the federal poverty level (FPL), pregnant women living near FPL, poor seniors (known as Medi-Medi or dual eligibles because they qualify for both Medicare and Medicaid), and people with disabilities who qualify for Supplemental Security Income (SSI) benefits based on their low income and resources. As reflected in Table 7, these limited eligibility rules kept Medicaid enrollment much lower than Medicare.

If states wanted to go beyond these segments, they would apply for and obtain waivers to expand coverage. In the lead-up to the ACA, some states applied for and obtained waivers to cover a broader range of low-income, non-disabled, non-pregnant adults.

As a consequence of these divergent perspectives, the Medicaid program has suffered from fragmented administration through the various state agencies. The program's adaptation over the past 50 years has been a complex, ad hoc process from state to state, with varying levels of competency, state funding, and attitudes towards social services, flowing from the philosophical tensions described above around poverty.

The challenges also extend to the beneficiary population, which is more difficult to manage than the Medicare population. The poorest Americans are also the most beset by pandemics like obesity and addiction, the most difficult to communicate with (by virtue of having large pockets of non-English speakers and the most difficult to reach), and have the most serious chronic health problems, such as heart disease, diabetes, asthma, and hypertension.

Medicare Expansion

In contrast to the divisive subject of Medicaid, as reflected on Table 7, enrollment in the politically popular Medicare program grew steadily over the decades. The contrast in the growth curves, Medicare relatively straight continuous growth and Medicaid with prolonged flatter stretches reflects the difference in their relative political popularity.

Table 7

Medicare and Medicaid Enrollment, 1966-Present

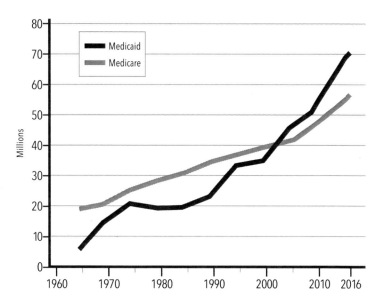

Source: Medicare and Medicaid enrollment (including fee-for-service and managed care) based principally on CMS and data reported by Kaiser Family Foundation.

Table 8

Total Medicare and Medicaid Spending, 1966 to Present

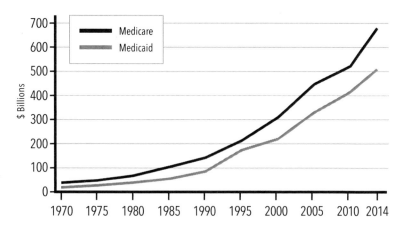

NOTE: Medicare spending is 100% federal. Medicaid spending in the aggregate is allocated roughly 60% federal and 40% spent by the states, with a variance as uneven as almost 80% federal and 20% state responsibility in Kentucky and as low as 50% federal and 20% state in Virginia.

Source: CMS, 2015; Office of Management and Budget, "Historical Tables: Budget of the United States Government, Fiscal Year 2012); Kaiser Family Foundation

Chapters 2 and 3 tell the story of how, over time, Medicaid eventually caught up and surpassed Medicare in terms of the numbers of program enrollees, with almost 30% growth in Medicaid enrollment numbers during President Obama's term (from 50 million people in 2009 to over 70 million in 2016). But even though Medicaid became the broader program when measured by the population served, it remained the lower burden on the federal government.

Both Medicare and Medicaid experienced breathtaking increases in cost, as illustrated in Table 8. Over five decades, the two programs have grown from $10 billion in the late 1960s to over $1 trillion in 2016.[2] Consider the numbers as part of the federal budget:

Taken together, Medicare and Medicaid represent roughly 22% of the entire federal budget. Medicare accounts for roughly 14% of the budget (60% of the combined expense for the two programs), and Medicaid accounts for about 8% of the federal budget.

What has accounted for the program growth? For Medicare, part of the story has been rising life expectancies, climbing into the 80s for significant segments of the population. The fastest-growing segment of the U.S. population today are centenarians. Despite the rising costs, it has taken time for politicians to work up the courage to call for a hike in the age for Medicare eligibility. (We address the prospect for a change to age 67 as part of TrumpCare.) As of today, Medicare offers various incentives to encourage people to consider deferring enrollment to age 70, but the decision to do so remains entirely voluntary.)

While Medicaid funding has also grown over the decades,

the growth has been attributable not to the growing percentage of people living in poverty, but to changes in public policy that have expanded the categories of low income Americans covered by the program. As we will see in Chapter 2, the ACA was the first successful reform effort to extend Medicaid to all people based on low income, irrespective of their age and ability to work.

Table 9
Medicare + Medicaid as a Share of the Federal Budget, 2014

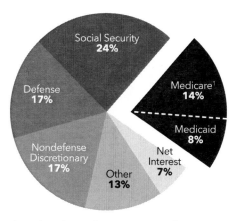

Total Federal Outlays, 2014 = $3.5 Trillion
Net Federal Medicare Outlays, 2014 = $505 Billion
Net Federal Medicaid Outlays, 2014 = $287 Billion

NOTE: All amounts are for federal fiscal year 2014. [1]Consists of Medicare spending minus income from premiums and other offsetting receipts. State expenditures on Medicaid are not shown on this table. [2]Includes spending on other mandatory outlays minus income from offsetting receipts.

Source: Congressional Budget Office, Updated Budget Projections: 2015 to 2025 (March 2015)

Even with the ACA Medicaid expansion, as reflected on Table 9, federal spending on Medicaid (about 8% of the federal budget) has been substantially less than on Medicare because the states bear roughly 40% of the Medicaid expense. The federal/state split on Medicaid spending is roughly 60/40 varying widely among the states, from as little as 51% federally funded in Massachusetts or Virginia to nearly 80% federally funded in Kentucky and Arkansas.[3]

Lingering Gaps in U.S. Healthcare Coverage

The Medicare and Medicaid patches on top of the preexisting system of employer-based coverage resulted in widespread coverage for the healthcare needs of the elderly from the late 1960s until today, but still left uninsured gaps in American society. While roughly 25 million Americans carried individual, non-employer private insurance coverage under the exchange, up to 50 million people have no coverage at all, mainly due to financial issues.

A huge number of poor Americans did not qualify for access to Medicaid benefits because their low incomes were not low enough to meet the state-established Medicaid levels, and they remained uninsured.

Many working class Americans had jobs that did not include health insurance as a benefit. While insurance was an expected benefit for professional and industrial jobs, many lower-paying, service sector jobs – driving a cab (like driving for Uber today) or waiting tables in a restaurant – did not include insurance. Ironically, in our experience, many healthcare facilities and other kinds of providers, from nursing homes to home health agencies, do not offer their employees health insurance or other benefits.

Even many entrepreneurs and self-employed people with small businesses forego insurance because of cost and limited resources. Some of these people are what we address in Chapter 2 as the healthy "young invincibles," but many are older small business owners.

Unemployed people also remained uninsured. As addressed in Chapter 2, the Consolidated Omnibus Budget

Reconciliation Act (COBRA), mandated a brief extension where people who lost their jobs could pay for their own insurance after termination, but there was no solution for the long-term unemployed. Other segments of the uninsured included those in prison, undocumented immigrants, and a sizeable number of Native Americans.

As a result of these various uninsured populations, in the lead-up to the Affordable Care Act, the percentage of uninsured Americans in the gap between employer coverage and Medicare or Medicaid grew steadily from roughly 12% of Americans in the late 1960s to 17% in the 1990s. This group represented 40 to 50 million Americans, with the largest segment being the working poor.

As we explore in Chapter 2, in the forty-something years from the early 1970s until 2010, there were numerous piecemeal efforts and several unsuccessful reform initiatives to close this insurance gap on the road to ObamaCare.

TWO:
THE STRANGE, WONKISH ROAD TO OBAMACARE

Timeline of U.S Healthcare Reform

1965: Creation of the Medicare and Medicaid programs

1972-74: Failure of Nixon and Kennedy Healthcare Reform Efforts

1974: Employee Retirement Income Security Act (ERISA)

1986: Emergency Medical Treatment and Labor Act (EMTALA)

1993: Failure of the Clinton American Health Security Act (AHSA)

2010: Enactment of the Affordable Care Act (ACA)

With an understanding from Chapter 1 of the underlying problems facing U.S. healthcare, we turn to the developments that led, over the course of the half-century following the launch of Medicare and Medicaid, to the Affordable Care Act.

The most interesting backstories about ObamaCare, given its reputation in the public mind as a liberal misadventure, are the Republican precursors of many of its key elements. Decades before it was nicknamed (derisively, in some quarters) ObamaCare, the healthcare reform model that became the Affordable Care Act began as a Republican vision.

> Decades before it was nicknamed (derisively, in some quarters) ObamaCare, the healthcare reform model that became the Affordable Care Act began as a Republican vision.

Nixonian Reform as a Predecessor of the ACA

The earliest versions of the model that became ObamaCare date back to the Nixon Administration. In the years after the 1965 enactment, Medicare and, to a lesser extent, Medicaid were popular. Aware of the gaps in access to healthcare, Democratic political leaders, most notably Massachusetts Senator Ted Kennedy, called for universal national health coverage. The national conversation around health insurance turned to competing visions of how to fill the remaining gaps in healthcare coverage left by the combination of the two federal laws and employer-based coverage.

The political battle line, at the time, was between two distinct models of universal coverage that would increase coverage for the working poor who lacked employer-based coverage. Senator Kennedy championed the liberal proposal: a "public option," meaning expansion of a broader healthcare entitlement within or alongside the Medicare and Social Security Programs.

44

President Nixon and his fellow Republicans responded to Senator Kennedy by advocating for a more limited, market-based approach to universal coverage: a private insurance solution that would compel larger employers to participate (i.e., an employer mandate), along with subsidized care (through federal funding of Medicaid) for the poor with dependent children. Nixon's proposal, the National Health Insurance Standard Act (NHISA), never got to the House floor for a vote.

Instead, Congress passed and Nixon signed into law the more modest Social Security Amendments of 1972, which extended Medicare to the long-term disabled and also to people with end-stage renal disease (ESRD).

In 1974, Nixon attempted to pass a broader bill, known as the Comprehensive Health Insurance Plan (CHIP). CHIP represented a more comprehensive approach: an employer mandate plus state-run health plans with subsidization for those who could not afford them. Ultimately, the Watergate scandal derailed both Nixon's healthcare reform effort and Kennedy's alternative before Nixon and Kennedy could reach agreement on a compromise.

As described in Chapters 3 and 4, the contrast between the Republican position in the 1970s and today reflects a significant political shift in terms of the party's perspective on the healthcare reform elements of an employer mandate, Medicaid expansion, and subsidization for those who cannot afford coverage. Concepts that were Republican proposals in the 1970s are rejected today. The consistent thread is a Republican philosophical preference for a private insurance-driven solution over a public expansion, driven, among other things, by concerns about how to control unchecked healthcare costs. At the same time, there has been a striking shift to a markedly tougher attitude toward what to do for those who cannot afford private insurance. As a result, we are considerably farther away today than we were four decades ago from a bipartisan consensus on how to make healthcare accessible to poor Americans.

Healthcare on the Backburner

After the Nixon-Ted Kennedy failure, healthcare reform spent almost two decades as a backburner political issue. At the risk of oversimplifying things, there were only minor adjustments in federal healthcare policy as other political issues took center stage.

Under President Gerald Ford, the most noteworthy change to federal healthcare law was the enactment of the Employee Retirement Income Security Act (ERISA). ERISA exempts large, self-insured employers from state regulations when they establish their own employee health (and other benefit) plans. Thanks to ERISA, small and large employer (generally over 150+ employees) health benefits operate under a completely different laws, setting up a distinct legal system within a system for large employers.

Healthcare reform did not advance under President Jimmy Carter although the federal agencies that administered it were renamed on his watch. In 1977, the agency that runs Medicare – the Centers for Medicare and Medicaid Services (CMS), known at the time as the Health Care Financing Administration (HCFA) – launched within the Department of Health, Education, and Welfare (HEW). In 1980, HEW was renamed the Department of Health and Human Services (HHS). President Carter proposed the Children's Health Assessment Program, an initiative to expand Medicaid for poor children, but this piece of healthcare legislation never came to a vote in Congress.

EMTALA: Reagan Era Socialized Medicine

Ironically, the largest expansion into "socialized medicine" occurred under the Reagan Administration in 1986. The Emergency Medical Treatment and Labor Act (EMTALA) was a response to the horror that ensued when a pregnant woman in the middle of a tough delivery was turned away from a private hospital emergency room (ER). Since 1986, EMTALA has required hospitals participating in federally-funded programs (i.e., virtually all hospitals) to provide care to any person presenting in their ER to the point of stabilization prior to inquiring about the patient's ability to pay or other financial issues. Prior to the ACA, this translated to 45 million uninsured presenting at hospitals nationwide, along with roughly 50 million underinsured Medicaid patients.

The largely unintended but nonetheless socialist effect of EMTALA and its cost-shifting was to address care provided to people who could not afford it by silently passing it on through hospital charges to the ratepayers of private insurance. Hospitals would have to hire or contract with physicians to deliver medical care and utilize resources for uninsured patients. To participate in federally-sponsored programs, they would need to provide not only ER physicians, but also specialty care consistent with that provided to Medicare beneficiaries: on call general surgeons, heart surgeons, interventional cardiologists, pulmonologists, and obstetricians to answer to the needs of any patient presenting in the ER, whether or not the patient is insured.

All of this ER call coverage was not free. Hospitals were forced to figure out how to pay physicians for their availability and to backfill any shortfalls in physician billings for patients unable to pay their bills. Where do hospitals get the money to pay for all this care? They need to aggressively negotiate with private insurers to make sure that the rates paid for insured patients not only cover the costs of care for those privately insured patients, but also generate enough money to cover the costs of the uninsured and underinsured who show up in the ER. In some geographies, this equation results in ratepayers paying almost double what they would otherwise pay.

While the majority of hospitals succeed in passing on the costs of care to the uninsured and underinsured to private insurance patients, another Reagan era law, the 1981 Medicaid Disproportionate Share (DSH) program, offered a second option. DHS payments by the state and federal government offset costs of care to the uninsured and underinsured for hospitals that disproportionately provide care to low-income and Medicaid patients.

Another noteworthy healthcare reform under President Reagan was the 1986 Consolidated Omnibus Budget Reconciliation Act (COBRA), under which EMTALA was passed. COBRA also included a requirement that companies with 20 or more employees offer terminated employees the option of staying on the employer insurance plan at the employee's own expense for up to 36 months. Various states also expanded these continuation and portability requirements to include a broader range of small employers. While COBRA guaranteed short-term, albeit costly post-employment healthcare coverage, the long-term unemployed remained an uncovered group.

Lessons from the Failure of HillaryCare
"For nearly two decades after Nixon, the pattern was a series of relatively narrow changes to healthcare laws." Efforts towards broader based health reform were essentially

dormant. The underlying issues – lingering gaps in healthcare access and runaway spending growth – did not go away, but other public policy challenges took center stage, until 1993, when the newly elected President Bill Clinton commissioned a task force led (with some controversy at the time) by then First Lady Hillary Clinton to review and recommend healthcare reform.

> "For nearly two decades after Nixon, the pattern was a series of relatively narrow changes to healthcare laws."

The Clinton proposal, formally known as the American Health Security Act (AHSA) but today better known as HillaryCare, envisioned the expansion to universal coverage mainly through private insurance providers managed by the government. Private health insurance would be offered through managed competitive marketplaces (precursors of the ACA exchanges), that would be coordinated by state-level regional health alliances. Like Nixon's proposal, the Clinton model included a mandate that employers provide health insurance, as well as an individual mandate for those who fell in the gap between employer coverage and Medicare or Medicaid.

Both the task force leading to AHSA and the bill itself drew broad opposition, and were essentially dead on arrival in Congress. It would take another 20 years before healthcare reform built on the central element of both the Nixon and Clinton models – a mandate for employers to cover their employees' healthcare insurance costs – would ultimately be enacted. The failure of AHSA and the controversy of the Clinton task force offered many lessons to the Obama administration and Congressional Democrats about pitfalls along the way to enactment.

> *The failure of AHSA and the controversy of the Clinton task force offered many lessons to the Obama administration and Congressional Democrats about pitfalls along the way to enactment.*

One key lesson was the need for insurance industry buy-in. One of the most famous episodes from AHSA's failure was success of the famous (or infamous) 1994 "Harry and Louise" television advertisement pitting government bureaucrats against hard working Americans. The influence of this ad highlighted the power of insurance industry, which worked hand in hand with the National Federation of Independent Businesses to attack the Clinton bill.

Where AHSA's architects failed to appreciate the danger of insurance industry opposition, the Obama administration and Congressional Democrats worked assiduously to get insurance industry buy-in, at the cost of allowing health plan lobbyists to play a leading role in shaping the ACA. While insurers agreed to some regulatory constraints in the process (such as medical loss ratios requiring them to spend 85% of premiums on healthcare), they were also guaranteed a leading role in the ACA, as individuals and large employers would be forced to buy coverage from the same private companies that helped write the law – without the prospect of having to compete with a government option.

Another lesson that the Obama administration learned from the failure of HillaryCare was the need to address middle class concerns. Opponents of the Clinton plan, including the insurance companies, defeated it by seizing on middle class anxiety over the bureaucratic nature of the plan and the potential increase in cost for people who already were getting their healthcare needs met in the existing system.

These fears touched a nerve. It didn't matter how much the Clinton "Health Security Express" bus tour had highlighted the glaring lack of access to affordable healthcare or the vulnerability of blue collar Americans. The middle class was spooked by the prospect of having to pay more for worse coverage forced on them by the government. As a result, the ACA messaging and roll-out tried to be more careful about letting people keep their existing plans (at least for a while). In Chapter 3, we'll examine the messaging battle that played to the anxiety of the already insured.

A Return to More Modest Reform
After the 1993 failure of the Clinton health reform initiative, the next dozen or so years were another relatively quiet time for healthcare. Under the Clinton administration, tweaks to healthcare law included the 1992 Stark laws against physician self-referral and the 1996 Health Insurance Portability and Accountability Act (HIPAA), establishing health data privacy and security standards. President Clinton signed into law the 1996 Mental Health Parity Act, a precursor of the 2008 similarly named law prohibiting health plan discrimination against mental health benefits. Medicare Part C, the precursor of the Medicare Advantage Plan (addressed in Chapter 4) was established in 1997, as was the State Children's Health Insurance Program (S-CHIP) block grant program to provide states funding for low-income children who did not qualify for Medicaid. S-CHIP, now known as CHIP, expanded coverage for children in poor families who did not qualify for Medicaid.

President George W. Bush's main contributions to healthcare were through his President's Emergency Plan for AIDS Relief (PEPFAR) that distributed retroviral drugs in Africa, his 2001 moratorium on stem cell research, and the Medicare expansion in 2003 that introduced Medicare Part D, the prescription drug benefit. Once again, Senator Ted Kennedy spurred the programmatic changes to Medicare, working with Orrin Hatch and other Republicans to prompt this Medicare expansion. Kennedy is credited with bringing other Democratic senators on board, despite personally voting against it. His opposition focused on the provisions allowing HMOs to compete with Medicare for patients. President Bush did propose a plan to reform the private health insurance market in 2007 that would have given everyone the same standard tax deduction for buying health insurance, no matter whether they bought it themselves or got it through their employer, and included an "Affordable Choices Initiative" for those who did not qualify for Medicaid. Democrats in Congress were not interested in working with President Bush on this issue, and the proposal died before a bill was even introduced.

More Recent Bipartisan Precedents for ObamaCare

While the Obama administration was plainly mindful of learning from the Clinton failures in the lead up to the ACA, it could have been forgiven for thinking that the outlines of the reform effort would yield bipartisan support. After all, Republican presidential candidate Mitt Romney had enacted a similar law in 2006 while he was governor of Massachusetts. Among other similarities to the ACA, RomneyCare (described in greater detail in Chapter 7 in a survey of state reform efforts) incorporated an individual mandate, insurance purchasing pools, and subsidization of those who could not afford to buy insurance. Curiously, Governor Romney credited the conservative Heritage

Foundation think tank as a source for the model, with some consternation from Republicans who now disavow these roots. RomneyCare was not the only Republican initiative linked to Heritage Foundation. Its vision was also linked to the 1993 Republican alternative to the Clinton Plan. When Governor Romney ran against President Obama in 2012, Democrats did not miss the opportunity to highlight the irony of Republican opposition to the ACA, given the points of commonality with RomneyCare.

After all, Republican presidential candidate Mitt Romney had enacted a similar law in 2006 while he was governor of Massachusetts

The Road to ObamaCare

Upon taking office in 2009, President Obama set healthcare as a public policy priority for his administration. While it is possible to articulate a driving motivation based on healthcare as a human rights issue, the likelier impetus seems to have been the Obama administration's economic analysis of the problem set out in Chapter 1. The U.S. accounted for roughly a quarter of worldwide gross domestic product (GDP) – approximately $15 trillion out of worldwide GDP of $60 trillion. Healthcare represented 18% of U.S. GDP, nearly $3 trillion. The magnitude of the imbalance was palpable in macroeconomic terms: one nickel out of every dollar of goods and services in the world was spent on U.S. healthcare. Despite this enormous expenditure, The U.S. ranked roughly 37th out of 42 so-called developed countries in most all measures of mortality and morbidity. These imbalances were not sustainable.

> *The U.S. ranked roughly 37th out of 42 so-called developed countries in most all measures of mortality and morbidity. These imbalances were not sustainable.*

President Obama is a pragmatist. He knew that scrapping the existing healthcare system and starting with a fresh slate was not politically feasible given the powerful and entrenched insurance, physician, hospital, and pharmaceutical lobbies who benefited in the status quo and had proven their ability to interject themselves into the legislative process.

As a politician, President Obama was not about to point the finger at American's individual behaviors as a root cause of the poor health results of the world's most expensive system. Instead, after his January 2009 inauguration, President Obama targeted healthcare reform as a signature initiative with care in addressing the underlying factors.

To lead the healthcare reform effort, he designated Kansas Governor Kathleen Sebelius as the point person, not just to run healthcare reform from the White House, but also to serve as Secretary of the Department of Health and Human Services (HHS). In the early months of his presidency, President Obama, Secretary Sebelius, and their team met with a broad swathe of industry stakeholders – insurance companies, doctors, hospital chains, pharmaceutical companies, consumer advocates, and legislators – a legislative process lesson hard learned from the Clinton task force's failures. They aligned effectively with Congressional Democrats in pursuit of health reform.

Obama and Single Payer

One interesting question was whether the model of ObamaCare was actually supported by President Obama himself. Perhaps the greatest irony of the name "ObamaCare" is that President Obama himself has stated on more than one occasion that, if he had a clean slate to work with, his personal choice would have been a single-payer system. Among Republicans, the suspicion from the outset was that President Obama's real goal was a universal coverage public option – the single-payer model harkening back to the early 1970s. Progressive Democrats in Congress were open about their desire for the Obama administration to push a single-payer option. As Bernie Sanders demonstrated in the 2016 Democratic primary, it's much easier to be passionate about an egalitarian concept like single payer than a compromise like the ACA.

> *President Obama himself has stated on more than one occasion that, if he had a clean slate to work with, his personal choice would have been a single-payer system.*

Regardless of Obama's personal feelings, it's apparent that the public option was not a politically viable path in 2009. (In Chapter 10, we explore whether and how single payer and universal coverage are likely to resurface in 2020 and beyond.) While Democratic progressives wanted single payer, centrists like Senator Joseph Lieberman were openly hostile to the idea. While the Democratic moderates might agree to expansion of Medicaid, they would join Republicans in opposing a broader single-payer vision that disrupted the Medicare/Medicaid structure on the grounds of both high cost and excessive government control. The insurance companies would steadfastly resist an option that required them to compete in the marketplace against the government. Doctors, hospitals, the pharmaceutical industry – more or less everyone providing healthcare – would likewise resist greater centralization of federal power represented by single-payer as a solution.

Beyond the financial issues, healthcare providers were increasingly wary of the federal government dictating how healthcare is delivered through measures like the CMS Conditions of Participation in Medicare (COPs). As we will explore in Chapter 4, Republicans have seized on healthcare industry concerns about big government encroachment on medical decision-making.

As a legislative realist facing the potential pitfalls of the Washington lobbying environment, President Obama and his administration instead pursued the same more moderate option that Nixon and Romney had also pursued. What emerged from the White House in 2009 was a wonkish set of compromises: not a grand vision – such as Medicare for everyone – but instead a cobbling together of complicated elements and formulas to move towards a solution. As the saying goes, a camel is a horse designed by committee. The ACA exemplified this design by committee approach.

President Obama worked assiduously to build a coalition of support. His administration, along with Congressional Democrats, met with all of the industry groups and other stakeholders. They negotiated a framework that had give-and-take elements for everyone.

The pharmaceutical industry, for example, agreed to pay $80 billion to support the insurance expansion, largely by expanding the Medicaid discount. In return, the Obama administration agreed not to allow HHS or the Medicare program to negotiate drug prices. Other "goodies" were also part of the bargain. The Obama administration negotiated to give drug companies items from their wish list, such as extended market exclusivity for biologics, meaning that pharmaceuticals could price biologics without the downward pressure price competition from generics. With these protections in place, Big Pharma supported the enactment of the ACA and did not use its lobbying might in ways that might have threatened the legislation.

The insurance industry went through similar negotiations. The ACA ensured that private insurance would be an even bigger part of the solution for access to U.S. healthcare. Had the advocates of a public option had their way, it is possible to imagine a scenario in which healthcare reform did not translate into tens of millions of new policyholders. Instead, to gain their support, the role of private insurance companies was "baked into" the ACA. The individual mandate would require every person to buy insurance if his or her employer or the government didn't already provide it. Employers over a certain size (50 FTEs) would be required under the mandate for large employers to provide insurance coverage. All of these requirements meant that the system would be locked into an insurance model.

In return, insurers agreed to limits on their profits, in the form of medical loss ratios requiring them to spend 85% of premiums on healthcare services. Insurers also agreed to cover people with preexisting conditions. They agreed to pay over $100 billion in new fees and taxes to fund the expansion efforts. Through these negotiations, the Obama administration secured a critical piece of the puzzle that President Clinton did not have 16 years earlier: insurance industry buy-in.

> *The Obama administration secured a critical piece of the puzzle that President Clinton did not have 16 years earlier: insurance industry buy-in.*

The American Medical Association (AMA) also came to the bargaining table. The single most disruptive part of the Medicare Fee-for-Service system – physician reimbursement – would also be the easiest to fix. After all, hospitals are paid per incidence of illness and get a flat fee for the patient's incidence of illness, regardless of how long the patient stays in the hospital. Doctors, on the other hand, are paid per visit. As a result, doctors have an inherent incentive to keep the patients in the hospital longer, while hospitals benefit from quicker discharges.

This simple misalignment causes enormous disruptions in hospital operations, and accounts for needless additional costs, as hospitals deploy in-house case managers and hospitalists to try to limit attending physicians' abuses in keeping patients in the hospital too long. In theory, the government had a relatively easy fix to align hospitals and doctors: pay everyone on an incidence of illness rather than per visit. Such a radical departure from the status quo, however, would have ensured the bitter opposition of ObamaCare by the AMA. As a result, the ACA never seriously considered a change in physician reimbursement that would depart from historical payment structures without additional reforms that would aid physicians. In fact, several of the early ACA initiatives actually focused on increasing physician reimbursement for treating Medicare patients. In this way, yet another interest group, physicians, bought in.

The negotiations continued with distinct segments of

healthcare stakeholders. In retrospect, some stakeholders did better than others. The drug companies fared well. For doctors, the ACA accelerated a migration from small and solo practices towards a predominant practice model of larger physician groups. A good case can be made that this transition, along with reimbursement changes, leaves many physicians worse off as a result of the ACA. Likewise, many insurance companies ultimately ended up paying dearly in the form of massive losses on plans offered through the ACA expansion. Given the difficult history of previous health reform legislation, President Obama deserves credit for building a tenuous coalition of support and focusing on what was achievable with his coalition.

On Capitol Hill, the Obama team worked with House Speaker Nancy Pelosi and Senate Majority Leader Harry Reid to ensure alignment with Congressional Democrats. The Democratic House majority, won in the 2006 midterm elections, offered an opportunity to pass legislation, despite the failure to win any Republican support. As we'll explore in Chapter 3, while Republicans lacked the votes to prevent the passage of the ACA in Congress, they effectively sowed the seeds of worry in many parts of the country about the implications of ObamaCare.

Finally, before the massive bill was brought forward, an elite working group of 15 stakeholder representatives met at the White House over a period of months, "horse trading" elements of the final package. Ironically, we cannot confirm that there was either a single hospital administrator or a practicing licensed physician was in the room.

The Features of ObamaCare
Over 1,800 pages long, the Patient Protection and Affordable Care Act (PPACA) reflected a series of calculated

political compromises intended to get buy-in from all stakeholders while moving healthcare in the direction of addressing all of the problems of cost, quality, access, and cost allocation.

> *Over 1,800 pages long, the Patient Protection and Affordable Care Act (PPACA) reflected a series of calculated political compromises intended to get buy-in from all stakeholders while moving healthcare in the direction of addressing all of the problems of cost, quality, access, and cost allocation.*

In order to provide coverage to individuals who previously had not been able to afford coverage or not had the option of buying their own coverage, the ACA called for a number of changes to insurance underwriting practices. Insurance companies would no longer be permitted to deny coverage based on preexisting conditions and adult children could remain on their parents' policies until age 26. On the state insurance exchanges (see below), rates would be based primarily on income, rather than age or health history. Anyone with health insurance, whether purchased through the ACA, provided by employers, or covered by Medicaid, would all get the same ten minimum essential benefits:

- Ambulatory outpatient care
- Emergency care
- Hospitalization
- Pregnancy, maternity, and newborn care
- Mental health and substance abuse services
- Prescription drugs
- Rehabilitative services and devices
- Preventive and wellness services including chronic disease management
- Laboratory services
- Pediatric services including vision and dental care

For the poorest Americans, the Medicaid program would be expanded from selective eligibility for the "poor and" (pregnant women, children, the disabled) to cover anyone living at 137% or lower of federal poverty Level (FPL). To understand FPL, take a look at Table 10:

Table 10
2016 Federal Poverty Level (FPL) Rates

Family Size	100% FPL	138% FPL	400% FPL
1	$11,770	$16,242	$47,080
2	$15,930	$21,983	$63,720
3	$20,090	$27,724	$80,360
4	$24,250	$33,465	$97,000
5	$28,410	$39,205	$113,640

Source: Federal Register, Vol. 81, No. 15, January 25, 2016.

FPL is the standard the government uses to define how low income has to be for a person or a family to be considered to be living under the "poverty line." As Table 10 illustrates, FPL is calculated by family size and is adjusted annually based on federal data. In 2016, for example, being 100% FPL, i.e., living at the poverty line, translated to income of $11,770 for individuals and $24,250 for a family of four. At 400% FPL, i.e. four times the poverty level, an individual earns $47,080 and a family of four earns $97,000 of household income. To put things in context, roughly 14% of the U.S. population (about 44 million Americans, more than the entire population of California) live at or below 100% FPL. Roughly 40% of Americans live at 400% FPL (about 128 million people).

The Medicaid expansion was driven by a recognition that subsidies and an insurance mandate were not going to be enough to help people living near the poverty line, and by a desire to clean up the historic problems with Medicaid gaps. The federal government would assume 100% of the cost for the initial three years (2014-16), followed by incremental reduction to 90% by 2020. To improve primary care access without delay, Medicaid would be paid at 100% of Medicare rates for 2013 and 2014.

Perhaps the trickiest problems that the ACA attempted to solve were the related questions of (1) how to ensure that individuals who were not covered by an employer health plan (or Medicare, Medicaid, or a state or federal health program) would in fact purchase health coverage under the new law and (2) how to ensure that the insurance companies would not lose too much money by not being able to charge higher premiums to individuals with preexisting conditions. The solution was the individual mandate, the requirement that any person not otherwise covered must buy health insurance policies from newly-created health insurance exchanges in order to avoid paying a tax penalty. The goal was to force enough "young invincibles" with lower health costs to buy in to offset the expensive older, sicker people coming into the exchanges with preexisting conditions.

> *The solution was the individual mandate, the requirement that any person not otherwise covered must buy health insurance policies from newly-created health insurance exchanges in order to avoid paying a tax penalty.*

The individual mandate was supposed to work like Social Security. We sometimes think about Social Security as a paycheck withdrawal that each of us is personally banking some amount for our retirement. (This is an often-expressed Republican vision and the healthcare model of Singapore, which we discuss in Chapter 10). In reality, the way that Social Security works is that today's workers are paying into a pool that is being spent now, so that the government has the funds to pay benefits today's retirees. The goal of the individual mandate (and the insurance exchange) initiatives was to apply the same mechanism to healthcare. As Table 6 in Chapter 1 illustrates, most people have relatively few health expenses until their later 50s and 60s. Younger, healthier people in their 20s, 30s, and 40s would be required by the mandate to buy insurance, paying premiums with relatively low healthcare needs that would offset and balance the expensive needs of older, sicker people. At least that was how it was supposed to work.

In order to establish this framework, the states would be required to establish health insurance exchanges, which, beginning in 2014, would function as new marketplaces through which individuals and small businesses would be able to buy health plans with the assistance (if they qualified) of premium tax credits and cost-sharing subsidies. At the same time, people not covered by an employer health plan, Medicare, Medicaid, or another state or federal health program would be required to buy a plan on the health insurance exchanges, with the assistance of sliding scale subsidies (in the form of tax credits) for those earning from 138% up to 400% of FPL.

Table 11 reflects how much coverage purchased on the exchange would be subsidized:

Table 11
Subsidies for Health Coverage for on the ACA Exchanges

FPL	Household Income	Maximum Percentage of Income Spent on Insurance Premium	Out-of-pocket Spending Limits
150%	$36,375	4.0%	$4,500
200%	$48,500	6.3%	$10,000
300%	$72,750	9.5%	$12,700
400%	$97,000	9.5%	$12,700

NOTE: These projections are based on a "Silver" tier health plan purchased via an ACA insurance exchange for a family size of four, using 2015 FPL data. Percentages are rounded to the closest decimal point. Subsidies are provided in the form of premium tax credits to cap premium and out-og-pocket spending.

Source: Obamacare Facts (citing HHS Notice of Benefit and Payment Parameters for 2014 Final Rule)

The sliding scale would subsidize premiums to ensure that the maximum personal cost was 2% of personal income for people living below 133% FPL, ratcheting up to as high as 9.5% of personal income for people living at 400% of FPL. The tax credits would also serve to limit the maximum out-of-pocket medical spending: at 400% FPL, an individual's expense would be capped at $6,350 and a family of four would have its expense capped at $12,700. Any uninsured person who failed to obtain coverage would be subject to a tax penalty tied to their income level.

Another change built into the ACA was the large employer mandate. Until the ACA, many companies provided health insurance optionally. A handful of states, such as Hawaii and Massachusetts, imposed mandates that employers provide health coverage, but the decision was largely voluntary by employers. The ACA proposed to make the decision involuntary for any employer with 50 or more full-time equivalent (FTE) employees. These employers would be required to offer full-time employees insurance coverage. If any of their employees received a tax credit for buying individual coverage through the exchange because they did not receive coverage as a benefit of employment, the employer would be subject to a tax penalty.

In addition to the foregoing mechanisms of insurance reform, the ACA also sought to improve quality and efficiency and reduce cost through a series of care coordination and integration initiatives. These included a variety of new payment and service delivery models that would be tested under the ACA as potential solutions to the cost/quality conundrum, looking for a transition away from volume-based "fee-for-service" reimbursement to value-based, more integrated and coordinated care.

The concept of shifting from paying for volume to paying for value had been a longstanding but elusive goal of health reform. In bringing down healthcare costs while improving quality, the most promising option was to shift from paying for inputs (i.e., the fee-for-service model of each service rendered by a doctor or hospital) to a value-based system where we pay for outputs (i.e., healthier patients, fewer readmissions) and outcomes. One model that the ACA sought to experiment with was bundled payment, through which Medicare would pay a lump sum to a health system for a period of care (e.g., before a hip replacement surgery, the surgery itself, and 45 days of post-surgical care). This method of payment shifted the cost risk downstream by requiring coordination and negotiation over pricing by providers for a fixed sum paid by government health programs and private payers. Another variation was payment for performance, a reimbursement model in which health professionals would be paid for how well they performed, utilizing indicators such as healthcare outcomes and patient satisfaction.

A number of the initiatives of the ACA, such as hospital readmissions penalties, were focused on incentivizing hospitals and other healthcare facilities to manage patients more proactively, to end the expensive revolving door of patients repeatedly coming back to the hospital. In general, the goal was to suppress hospital overutilization, by motivating hospitals to step down patients to the lowest cost setting of care in which the patient could be handled.

One of the most prominent of numerous care coordination and integration initiatives was the Accountable Care Organization (ACOs). ACOs were self-organized networks of providers (most commonly, hospitals and doctors), who align to share the responsibilities of providing patients with coordinated care across the continuum, sharing information and reducing unnecessary care, saving money in the process. Pushing the boundaries, ACOs utilized different payment formulas that reward quality metrics instead of quantity metrics.

Other initiatives were designed to increase the efficiency and quality of American healthcare through research programs. The new CMS Innovation Center was charged with testing new payment and service delivery models, such as the Bundled Payments for Care Improvement, a pilot program to bundle payments to providers and establish value-based purchasing for Medicare, Medicaid, and CHIP.

The ACA also provided $10 million for the establishment of a new nonprofit, the Patient-Centered Outcomes Research Institute (PCORI), an independent organization that funds comparative clinical effectiveness research. PCORI's mission is to support accessible research that will help patients, clinicians, and insurance companies to make informed decisions when choosing treatment options, thereby improving outcomes.

Passage of ObamaCare

Despite some Republican input and cooperation during the initial development of the bill during the summer of 2009, by the time the bill came to a vote there was significant political pressure on Republicans to vote against the ACA. The legislative process shifted into high gear in November 2009, when the House of Representatives narrowly approved its version of ObamaCare by a 220-215 vote. The opposition included 39 Democrats, who joined Republicans in opposition to the bill.

The focus then shifted to the Senate. The August 2009 death of Senator Ted Kennedy, the healthcare reform stalwart, had left Senate Democrats one vote shy of the 60 needed for a supermajority to overcome a Republican filibuster. In September 2009, the supermajority was briefly restored by the appointment of Democrat Paul Kirk to Senator Kennedy's seat, until a special election could be held. With Senator Kirk's vote

Senate Democrats passed their version of ObamaCare on a

straight party line vote on Christmas eve.

At this point, the House and the Senate had passed similar, but not identical bills. The ordinary legislative clean-up process to reconcile the two versions was still ahead. The challenge was that, in January 2010, Senator Kirk lost the Massachusetts special election to Republican Scott Brown, who had made the opposition to ObamaCare a cornerstone of his campaign. Kirk's surprise defeat left Congressional Democrats in a quandary. They no longer had the 60 Senate votes needed to overcome a Republican filibuster.

Democrats found their solution in the budget reconciliation process, which allowed them to have a common bill approved by the House and the Senate based on a simple majority of 51 Senators. Both the House and Senate passed the Patient Protection and Affordable Care Act (PPACA) in March 2010, and President Obama signed it on March 23.

> *Democrats found their solution in the budget reconciliation process, which allowed them to have a common bill approved by the House and the Senate based on a simple majority of 51 Senators.*

Despite the fact that this was the most significant change to U.S. healthcare regulation in 50 years, the steadfast Republican opposition had forced Democrats to move forward without the thorough clean-up process that most legislation undergoes. The messier-than-usual language of the bill would come back to be a recurring issue in later Supreme Court battles.

Eight months after President Obama signed the bill into law, the Democrats lost their House majority in the 2012 midterm elections, shifting the battleground to Republican advantage. One important consequence of a House Republican majority hostile to the bill was to prevent the Obama administration the ability to adjust to unforeseen circumstances. As we'll explore in Chapter 3, the result was a mixed story of soaring triumph and bitter defeat for parts of the ACA.

THREE:
THE GOOD, THE BAD, AND THE UGLY OF OBAMACARE IMPLEMENTATION

One of the big challenges in writing about ObamaCare is the radically dxifferent and legitimate narratives that can be presented as part of the story. President Obama, the Congressional Democrats who passed it, and, as of this writing, the roughly half of Americans who continue to support the ACA can rightfully celebrate its remarkable triumphs. Chief among these is the expansion of access to care for more than 20 million previously uninsured Americans. The insurance exchanges extended coverage to over 12 million people. The Medicaid expansion under the ACA increased by over 7 million, and if compared from enrollment at the beginning of President Obama's presidency, actually expanded Medicaid from covering roughly 50 million Americans in 2009 to over 70 million today. Together, the percentage of uninsured Americans fell from 16-17% down to roughly 9%, the lowest level in a half century.

While the U.S. still has a sizeable uninsured population, the gap was significantly narrowed. For Americans who benefited by getting coverage previously unavailable to them, the law was a blessing. From this vantage point, the

ACA successfully addressed a serious problem – lack of healthcare access – that persisted through seven prior presidential administrations.

At the same time, critics of the ACA, including the incoming Trump administration, Congressional Republicans, and the roughly half of Americans who oppose the ACA, can correctly point to numerous failures, including the failure of the insurance exchanges to contain skyrocketing premiums and healthcare costs. Table 12 reflects how insurance premiums continued to increase as the ACA unfolded.

Table 12

Rising Insurance Premiums, 2008-2014

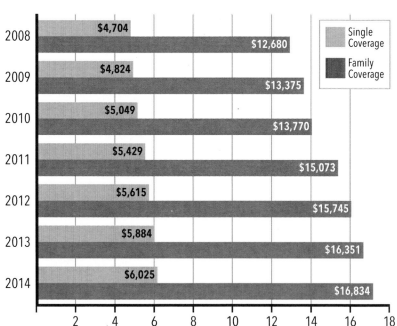

*Estimate is statistically different from estimate for the previous year shown (p<.05)
Source: Kaiser/HRET Survey of Employer-Sponsored Health Benefits, 1999-2014

For Americans who had decent coverage through their employer or Medicare before the ACA, the net impact of all of the change was paying more for less as costs went up even as the value of the insurance benefit eroded. While Table 12 illustrates rising costs of employer-based coverage, the escalation was significantly higher for individual coverage purchased on the health insurance exchanges. Even if some of these shortcomings were explainable, the Republican critiques go far broader than the practical failures to a rejection of the ACA as a collection of big government disasters.

Defining the ACA as a success or failure in large part stems from philosophical choices about the role of government in healthcare. Can healthcare delivery function well through the private market? Alternatively, are there sufficient market defects and social concern to treat healthcare as a universal insurance "right" or social benefit of living in the United States, like national defense and public education? These conflicting perspectives are not merely abstract, but played out over a messy seven years from 2010 to the present. From day one after its enactment, the ACA was a flashpoint of controversy and political battle. These fights manifested in over 60 separate Republican attempts to repeal the ACA and three Supreme Court decisions relating to the law. These battles shaped the implementation in critical ways.

> Defining the ACA as a success or failure in large part stems from philosophical choices about the role of government in healthcare.

In this chapter, our goal is to break through the rhetoric and take a hard look at what succeeded, what failed, and what lessons – positive and negative – can be learned from the years of ObamaCare implementation.

ACA Timeline

2010: ACA enacted

2013: Itemized Deductions for Unreimbursed Medical Expenses increased to 10% AGI; FSA contributions limited to $2,500/year

2014: Insurance exchanges open for individuals; individual mandate and new coverage rules took effect

2015: Employer mandate for business with over 100 full time equivalent (FTE) employees

2016: Employer mandate for business with over 50 FTEs

2018: Cadillac tax on high-cost insurance

ObamaCare Implementation

The implementation of the ACA was a massive project. It involved over 90 separate initiatives, each with its own legal provisions. Looking back over the past seven years, the law brought achieved an incredible amount of change, which presents a challenge to Republican lawmakers considering what can be undone and how to undo it.

Not every provision of the ACA was implemented. In several cases, laws were enacted, but the regulations needed to give them force were not promulgated or were significantly delayed. It is useful to review the highlights of the implementation process, as a backdrop to the critiques and battles that followed.

2010: Laying the Groundwork

The ACA began with a series of "baby steps" in 2010. Of the well-known ACA elements, the only one that began in 2010 was the requirement that insurance companies allow adult children up to age 26 to remain on their parents' policies. Among several dozen other initiatives, the 2010 roll-out of the ACA included:

A government process to review unreasonable insurance premium increases by health plans, requiring insurance companies to justify and post publicly rate increases more than 10%

Establishment of the Patient-Centered Outcomes Research Institute (PCORI) to conduct comparative clinical effectiveness studies of medical treatments

Tax credits for small employers (25 or fewer employees) with average annual wages of less than $50,000 that provide health insurance for employees

Authorization for the FDA to grant 12-year exclusivity for biologic drugs

A temporary program to provide health coverage to individuals with pre-existing medical conditions who have been uninsured for at least six months

2011: ACA Ramp-Up

In 2011, the first full year of the ACA, many of the insurance underwriting reforms took effect. The medical loss ratio requirements required insurance companies to refund clients if they spent less than 85% on clinical services (insurance claims and improving healthcare, as opposed to administrative, marketing or other operating costs) for large employer group plans, and 80% for individual and small employer group plans. Under the 80/20 rule, carriers had to spend at least 80% of premium dollars – and 85% for small business group premiums – on insurance claims and improving healthcare, while the other 20% could go toward administrative, marketing and other operating costs. In addition, if the insurer cannot prove it used 80% toward care, then the policy holders receive a rebate.

Starting in March 2011, the Department of Health and Human Services (HHS) distributed $49 million in grants to set up the state exchanges for individuals to buy insurance and to establish the Small Business Health Options Program (SHOP) that would be opened in 2014.

In order to be able to improve the efficacy of the healthcare industry, the ACA provided for several new mechanisms to evaluate payment models and spur innovation. A 15-member Medicare Independent Payment Advisory Board (IPAB) would be nominated by the President and Senate and approved by Congress, to submit legislative proposals containing recommendations to reduce the per capita rate of growth in Medicare spending if spending exceeds targeted growth rates. The Center for Medicare and Medicaid Innovation (CMMI) was established as part of the Centers for Medicare and Medicaid Services (CMS). Tasked with developing and testing new models for payment and service delivery, CMMI's programs evaluate new models of payment and care for Medicare, Medicaid, and CHIP, as well as accountable care organizations (ACOs), and try to speed up the implementation of best clinical practices.

2012 Medicare Changes

The ACA legislated several significant changes to Medicare in 2012. Over the course of the year, over 100 ACOs joined the pilot program to organize Medicare providers into groups that would share cost savings if they met certain quality thresholds. CMS implemented a Medicare Value-

Based Purchasing program to pay hospitals based on performance on quality measures and required plans to be developed to implement value-based purchasing programs for skilled nursing facilities, home health agencies, and ambulatory surgical centers. The ACA also established a new rule reducing Medicare payments for "excess" preventable hospital readmissions and making hospitals more publicly accountable for their readmission rates.

2013 Tax and Payment Adjustments

2013 brought further changes to Medicare, when 500 organizations joined the Bundled Payment pilot program, designed to develop and evaluate making bundled payments for acute, inpatient hospital services, physician services, outpatient hospital services, and post-acute care services for an episode of care. This type of bundled payment was intended to promote efficiency and coordination of care across providers.

In anticipation of more patients having health insurance under the state exchanges, hospitals agreed to give up 75% of Medicare Disproportionate Share Hospital (DSH) payments while states reduced their Medicaid DSH allotments. New payments for Medicare DSH would be tied to state percentages of uninsured individuals and the amount of care the hospitals provided.

A 2.3% excise tax on medical devices was imposed as way to bring an estimated $3 billion a year in additional revenue to fund parts of the ACA. Manufacturers would have to pay the tax on the sale of large items such as MRI machines, pacemakers, and artificial joints, as well as smaller items in physician's offices, such as tongue depressors. Items that consumers usually bought, like eyeglasses and hearing aids, were specifically exempt from this tax.

2014: Individual Mandate, Insurance Requirements and Medicaid Expansion

The central features of the ACA went into effect in 2014. As of January 1, individuals were required to purchase health insurance through the state exchanges or SHOP if they did not have employer-provided coverage or else pay a tax penalty. Similarly, companies with more than 50 employees would be fined if they did not offer healthcare coverage to their employees. Insurers, in turn, were required to offer an essential health benefits package that covered preventative and critical care as part of any health plan to any individual, regardless of preexisting conditions and without annual limits on coverage. Insurance ratings would be based on age, family size, geographic location and tobacco use.

The state exchanges would be a central website for applying for health coverage from private companies, and for those who were eligible, Medicaid and CHIP. Applicants would enter income and family composition information to determine what level type of insurance and how much assistance, if any, they would receive. If their individual income were 133-400% of the 2014 Federal Poverty level ($15,521-$46,680), they would receive premium subsidies in the form of tax credits, while those in the lower range (under 250% of the FPL, or $29,175) were eligible for more substantial cost sharing assistance. Anyone whose income was below 138% of the FPL ($16,104) would be eligible for Medicaid. This expansion of Medicaid also expanded presumptive eligibility programs, whereby hospitals could screen and enroll any Medicaid eligible individuals.

The Good: What the ACA Accomplished

The Obama administration deserves credit for enacting legislation that had been the subject of debate without much progress since the Nixon administration. President

Obama set his sights on a workable healthcare initiative and campaigned on it in 2008. After the election, his proposal went through numerous iterations in the House and Senate.

Ultimately the Affordable Care Act emerged and was enacted in 2010, providing a victory for Obama by accomplishing the seemingly impossible task of providing avenues to healthcare insurance for all Americans. The results included roughly 12-13 million newly insured people acquiring private health insurance plans through the Affordable Care Act exchanges, Medicaid expansion of roughly 7 million, and reduction of uninsured Americans to historical lows, according to the Kaiser Family Foundation. If you count pre-ACA Medicaid and CHIP expansion through grants from the beginning of President Obama's presidency, the actual increase enrollment in Medicaid alone went from roughly 50 million in 2009 to 70 million today.

In the two years since it was fully implemented, the ACA has had measurable effects on the healthcare marketplace and types of coverage. These effects include areas that were intended to fix perceived flaws in the system, including the expanded definition of incidental medical benefits, which addressed longstanding inconsistencies and gaps in care such as mental health, addiction treatment, prescription benefits, treatment for developmental disabilities, and pregnancy. Similarly, ACA provided basic wellness benefits (flu shots) and minimum coverages in the panoply of "metal" plans which gave Americans robust coverages in the new programs, and not just catastrophic event support. Accountable Care Organizations (ACOs) and other quality initiatives are also showing some promise, but it is too early to call them a definitive success.

The Bad: Where the ACA Fell Short

The ACA suffered numerous setbacks and unexpected challenges as the various pieces of the law went into effect. Even before President Trump won the presidency promising to repeal the ACA, the individual mandate and the insurance exchanges were a failure, as was the effort to rein in rising health insurance costs.

The Failure to Bring in Younger People

The ACA was a failure in terms of attracting younger people. Many of these younger consumers weighed the costs of participating in ObamaCare versus the tax penalties associated with opting out and chose the cheaper option – which in most cases was opting out. The penalties were just too weak to be a compelling reason to enroll in ObamaCare, and the premiums became increasingly onerous for young people facing low employment and staggering student loan debt. In fact, soaring premiums and high out-of-pocket costs made healthcare out of reach for many, resulting in angry consumers of all ages.

Rising Healthcare Costs

A further issue was the problem of cost. Many people think of the problem of U.S. healthcare not in terms of quality or lack of access, but in terms of how it affects their pocketbook, meaning how much out-of-pocket cost they will bear. As a measure of success, this set ObamaCare (and any alternative) up for failure.

The truth is that, with the influx of so many people with chronic problems who were previously uninsurable as a result of preexisting conditions, healthcare costs were bound to go up substantially, and they did. The problem was addressed through traditional some traditional insurance risk management steps, spreading the risk to a large pool of insureds.

The theory was that all of the "young invincibles" who were avoiding healthcare insurance because they were healthy would offset the costs because they would now be forced to buy coverage. The problem was that the penalties for not buying insurance were minimal, so they opted to pay the penalty. Thus the pools were not as large as anticipated, and the persons participating in pools were, on average, much sicker than anticipated. Another ACA change, allowing people to stay on their parents' insurance until age 26, also shrank the potential pool paying in.

Second, the expanded definition of minimum essential benefits to include things that had not been previously covered, including specialty drugs and behavioral health services like addiction treatment and developmental services for kids on the autism spectrum, also meant that costs were going up. While these additional services were extremely valuable to the people who received them, they come with high price tags. As a result, no one should have been surprised that plan benefits got worse and that out-of-pocket costs went up. The minimum essential benefit expansion expanded costs for employer-based plans, not only for people buying coverage on the exchanges. Unfortunately, people are slow to wake up to the reality that more and more healthcare costs are going to be borne by people as out-of-pocket expenses.

For the first three years of the ACA, the impact of the high-cost patient in the exchange pools was muted, largely because government-funded reinsurance subsidized health plans for enrolling higher-cost patients, with the goal of maintaining affordability and allowing the exchange plans to remain stable and attract more customers. As costs continued to spike, thanks to utilization of the new insurance coverage, reports of huge increases in plan prices made the news.

Miscalculations: From Healthcare.gov to Risk Corridor Shortfalls

The challenge of enacting sweeping legislation unilaterally with a narrow congressional majority led the Democrats little margin for error when mistakes arose. Perhaps the emblematic mistake of ACA implementation was the debacle of the October 2013 launch of the federal insurance exchange, www.healthcare.gov. The website launch was essential to enable people to buy subsidized insurance in advance of the January 2014 deadline as the individual mandate took effect.

Unfortunately, the healthcare.gov website was a planning disaster. It was not ready and repeatedly crashed and failed to deliver the information people needed or allow them enroll, suppressing enrollment. Republicans and the media had a field day with the demonstrable incompetence of the project. Ultimately, it forced an extension of the January 2014 deadline until the end of March 2014 to allow consumers more time to enroll as the administration scrambled to fix the website.

Another example of ACA "black eye" was the estimated shortfall of $2.4 billion in the risk corridors program, one of several stabilization measures that was used to bolster the health exchanges. The idea was that more profitable insurance plans would pay money into a fund to subsidize losses resulting to insurers for care of high cost patients brought into the system by the ACA. Unfortunately, someone's math was off, and the first year raised only $362 million against obligations of $2.87 billion to plans that lost money. While the larger insurance companies survived, in some cases with financial losses that led them to decide to withdraw from offering plans on the insurance exchanges, the debacle led to the insolvency and closure of the many nonprofit insurance cooperatives that had been formed to service newly covered patients and facilitate competition on the exchanges.

The list of ACA failures could be far longer, but these two examples are emblematic of numerous difficulties that arose throughout the ACA implementation. There were many missed deadlines (Republicans point to four out of five missed statutory deadlines in the span of one year) and delays in implementation. On some level, it is not surprising that there were unanticipated problems in a project with such ambitious sweep. Unfortunately for the Obama administration, the change in political control of Congress that occurred in the 2010 midterm elections eliminated any margin for Democrats to use legislation to allocate additional funding to address the issue or otherwise correct mistakes in the parts of the ACA that weren't working, like the individual mandate.

The Ugly: Republican "Jiggery-Pokery"
From the outset, the Republican attack on the ACA was blistering. The title is not intended to suggest that all of the Republican attacks were unjustified. It is useful to understand the legitimate difference of opinions and critique, which we address below. But what stands out was the extreme rhetoric that went over the line from honest and serious disagreement to sometimes nonsensical and dishonest fear-mongering. Given the magnitude of the problems and the complexity solution, one might have hoped for bipartisan effort directed at making the healthcare

system work better. Instead, Republicans resorted to jiggery-pokery (or, if you prefer, argle bargle) focused on generating emotional opposition to the ACA for political advantage.

Republican Objections to Big Government

From the Republican perspective, ObamaCare was a disaster. The central Republican attack on the ACA was that, like other policies of President Obama, the ACA was out of touch with American values. ObamaCare, Republicans told their constituents, was not about expanding healthcare, but about creeping Northern European-style socialism – expanding the reach of government over even more of the economy, creating bureaucracy and new government entitlements programs, and disregarding individual liberty by forcing people to buy insurance. It was a threat to free markets and individual freedoms, taking the worst kind of big government approach to how healthcare decisions are made.

> ObamaCare, Republicans told their constituents, was not about expanding healthcare, but about creeping Northern European-style socialism – expanding the reach of government over even more of the economy, creating bureaucracy and new government entitlements programs, and disregarding individual liberty by forcing people to buy insurance.

Republicans complained that the ACA was tax and expense nightmare: over two dozen new taxes on Americans totaling over a trillion dollars and billions of dollars lost to fraud, waste, and abuse. Everyone suffered. Healthcare costs skyrocketed for employers and individuals, leading to higher insurance premiums and narrower networks that limited consumer choices of healthcare providers. The higher healthcare costs also stalled job growth, as more employers hired part-timers to avoid expenses.

Further, the ACA disincentivized poor Americans from working because, as they earned more, they would lose Medicaid coverage or get diminished insurance subsidies. The Medicaid program was a disaster before the law, between its cost and access issues, and yet Democrats "swelled the rolls of Medicaid," making a bad program worse.

Whether you agree or disagree with their critique, these Republican philosophical objections to the ACA deserve respectful consideration. Smart people can disagree about how much of the solution to healthcare is public and private, about big government and small government approaches. As we'll explore in Chapter 4, the Republicans have a different vision that we believe merits exploration.

Beyond the particularities of healthcare, it is also interesting to consider the question of a broader Republican concern with government entitlement programs. Social Security and Medicare have built constituencies that depend upon them and will vote to defend those programs. The ACA was going to bring millions of new people under the tent of its benefits and make them dependent on the government. In 2012, Governor Mitt Romney was excoriated for private comments that "47%" of Americans were freeloading – paying no taxes and depending on government entitlement programs – and likely to be loyal Democratic supporters who would vote to continue and expand programs they depended on. While Romney was excoriated, his comment point to an underlying concern about entitlement creep.

The Fear Campaign

Beyond any legitimate objections, Republican pundits found a target-rich environment in ObamaCare. The biggest and worst scare tactic was the charge that the Obama administration would be unveiling "death panels" to ration care and decide who would live and die. This unfair caricaturization served to inflame voters and whip up fear.

Republicans repeatedly seized on uncontroversial, good government initiatives and imagined baselessly that they had sinister intentions. The Independent Payment Advisory Board (IPAB) became a death panel, when in fact it was a fairly boring mechanism to establish accountability for managing a longstanding problem of steadily rising Medicare reimbursement payments that exceeded federal spending limits. In reality IPAB was empowered only to make recommendations concerning cuts to provider rates for certain services if cost control goals were not met. Characterizing this as an Obama instrument to let people die was false and manipulative.

Republicans charged that there was a hidden agenda in the Patient-Centered Outcomes Research Institute (PCORI), an effort intended to provide physicians and patients with evidence-based data on what treatments were more and less effective to support better decision-making and health outcomes. In fact, claimed Republicans, President Obama will use this to dictate what care your doctor would provide you.

Republicans also managed to find a target in the Center for Medicare and Medicaid Innovation (CMMI), which was tasked with the fairly innocuous work of promoting and evaluating multiple care delivery and payment models through negotiations with individual provider groups. Republicans charged that the secret goal of initiatives like bundling payments to hospitals was to take over patient case management. Here, too, the goal was to incentivize efficiency in care choices, but Republicans claimed the agenda was to take decisions away from doctors.

The irony of Republican rhetoric was that all of these ACA initiatives were directed at the shared goal of reducing expense while improving the quality of care. But the goal seemed to be generating outrage, rather than understanding, towards ObamaCare.

Other conservative-driven scare tactics included raising the specter of the bankruptcy of the United States due to excessive healthcare costs. House Speaker John Boehner even contended that under Obamacare, there was a "net loss" of those covered. (All these arguments got four Pinocchios from the Washington Post's Fact-Checker, which tracks outlandish statements.)

The arguments were clever, however, despite their falsity, because they simplified a complex issue and scared voters. Some of the blame rests with President Obama and other Democratic leaders, who failed to develop effective messaging to tout ACA successes and call out Republicans when they slipped into demagoguery.

Meanwhile, Republicans seized on ACA failures as a political strategy and worked diligently to sow the seeds of discontent. The first warning sign of their effectiveness came in 2010, when Scott Brown won a special election to fill the seat held by Senator Ted Kennedy after Kennedy's death. Brown devoted particular attention to opposing healthcare reform as an un-American form of big government. The argument resonated, contributing to Democratic setbacks in the 2010 midterm elections.

Separate and apart from this analysis, there is a lesson about effective messaging. Although we saw in Chapter 2 how the Obama administration learned from the Clinton errors in co-opting stakeholders to enact the ACA, once the law was in place, they were solidly beaten in the court of public opinion. The Republicans won the messaging war, mobilizing intense opposition to a complicated law that would have been expected to draw more head-scratching than anger, given the enormity of the stakes. There are important lessons for the future of healthcare reform about managing the messaging.

> *The Republicans won the messaging war, mobilizing intense opposition to a complicated law that would have been expected to draw more head-scratching than anger, given the enormity of the stakes.*

The Three Supreme Court Battles

Leaving aside the issue of which critiques of the ACA were legitimate and which were not, the disagreements led to lawsuits challenging the ACA and, ultimately, to the Supreme Court decisions. Between 2012 and 2015, the Supreme Court revisited the constitutionality of the ACA three times. These decisions shaped the implementation of the ACA in critical ways.

Supreme Court Round 1: National Federation of Independent Business v. Sebelius (2012)

The first Supreme Court decision, NFIB v. Sebelius, came out in the summer of 2012. Several of the early challengers to the ACA were Republican-led states, including Florida, which filed a legal challenge to the constitutionality of the individual mandate.

Republicans argued that ObamaCare unconstitutionally violated state rights and personal autonomy by requiring individual citizens who didn't have coverage through employment, Medicare, or Medicaid to buy health insurance on the exchanges or pay a penalty when filing their taxes. Republicans also challenged whether states were required to expand their Medicaid programs and whether HHS Secretary Sebelius had exceeded her authority. Lower courts had split on these questions, with decisions both upholding and invalidating the law.

Based on the Court's majority of conservative, Republican-appointed justices, many assumed that the Supreme Court would strike down the ACA in its entirety. The decision came as a huge surprise – treated as an act of heroism by Democrats and betrayal by Republicans – when Chief Justice John Roberts surprised many by siding with the Court majority to uphold the ACA individual mandate. His reasoning re-read the individual mandate as a tax, which was safely within federal power to impose: "The [ACA] requirement that certain individuals pay a financial penalty for not obtaining health insurance may reasonably be characterized as a tax," wrote Roberts in the majority opinion. "Because the Constitution permits such a tax, it is not our role to forbid it, or to pass upon its wisdom or fairness."

Chief Justice Roberts deserves credit for withstanding pressure from the ideological conservatives on the Court, including Justices Scalia, Thomas, and Alito. (While Justice

Kennedy has also broken with conservative colleagues on a number of personal liberty issues, he stood with the conservatives on the ACA). Republicans and conservatives condemned Roberts' decision to uphold the individual mandate and, by extension, the mechanics of the law.

While Democrats celebrated the upholding of the individual mandate because it kept the ACA alive, many people overlooked the more complicated other piece of the Court's ruling, where Roberts voted with the conservative bloc of justices, saying the federal government could not force states to expand their Medicaid programs because the states had not received adequate notice to obtain their consent. The decision deemed the ACA Medicaid expansion to be a "shift in kind, not merely degree," because it transformed Medicaid from an aid program for discrete categories of poor people (the elderly, disabled, and families with children) into a form of "universal health insurance coverage." This perspective echoed the original and ongoing conservative concern about overbroad anti-poverty measures. Democrats were able to claim a victory in this case, but probably underestimated the negative effects of losing the Medicaid issue.

As a consequence of this second prong of the Supreme Court ruling, the door was opened to states to choose whether or not they wanted to participate in the Medicaid expansion.

Over the next four years, roughly two-thirds of states would elect to accept federal funds and expand Medicaid. The other third, Republican-led, would hold out. Table 13 shows a state-by-state map of which states expanded and which states held out.

Table 13

Obamacare and Medicaid: Hold-outs vs. Expansion States

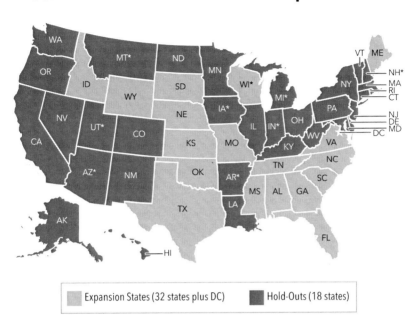

Expansion States (32 states plus DC)   Hold-Outs (18 states)

NOTES: *AR, AZ, IA, IN, MI, MT, and NH approved Section 1115 waivers. WI covered adults up to 100% FPL, without adopting ACA expansion. UT Medicaid expansion was APPROVED IN 2016 FOR A NARROWER SCOPE of beneficiaries.

Source: Kaiser Family Foundation

These decisions would turn out to create a strange disparity between the quality of life for people who lived in states that accepted funding and expanded Medicaid (expansion states) and those who lived in states that declined the expansion funds and maintained the limited, traditional Medicaid contours (hold-out states).

In the expansion states, expanded Medicaid coverage translated to dramatically improved access to healthcare. To use California as an example, prior to President Obama's election, roughly just under 1 in 5 Californians, approximately 7 million individuals received Medicaid (known as Medi-Cal). In the lead-up to the ACA, California applied for and received a federal grant, a Section 1115

Waiver known as "the Bridge to Reform" to begin transitioning the large population living at or just above the federal poverty level (FPL) to Medi-Cal, rather than waiting for the ACA expansion.

Between this preparatory expansion and the actual ObamaCare expansion, by 2015 the number of Californians on Medi-Cal grew to roughly 12 million, or nearly 1 in 3 Californians. Large health systems, community clinics, and many providers expanded their resources to meet the needs particular Medicaid-heavy communities. The number was expected to increase over the next 5 years to roughly 16 million people on Medi-Cal, or roughly 40% of Californians.

None of this should be taken to suggest that simply conferring Medicaid beneficiary status was, by itself, a panacea. There is a difference between improved access to healthcare and healthcare itself. Many of the practical complaints about ObamaCare – high deductibles in the private insurance world, and narrow networks and difficulty finding an available physician willing to accept the specific insurance policy or Medicaid – were legitimate complaints and critiques of the ACA implementation. These were the bugs that needed to be worked out of the system. Nonetheless, it was a sea change to move the conversation from whether or not the poorest Americans should be covered to the practical challenges of getting them doctors.

By contrast, the target population in hold-out states were still at square one. They did not participate in this newfound access to coverage or care. Instead, the only thing that the federal government could offer people at 137% of FPL or below in hold-out states was subsidies on the health insurance exchanges. (Many Republican-led states also declined to open exchanges, but the federal government gave residents of these states access via healthcare.gov, a federal exchange, which would be the subject of the 2015 Supreme Court decision in King v. Burwell, discussed below.)

These private insurance plans on the exchanges, with deductibles and coinsurance, were of little use to people who were too poor to be able to bear these expenses. High deductibles were a big challenge for middle-class Americans, but they were a complete barrier to access for people living at the poverty line. Writing for the New York Times, journalist Inara Verzemnieska captured the miserable condition of residents of what she called these ObamaCare "Dead Zones." In the Dead Zones, Republican governors had the satisfaction of blocking the ObamaCare vision, while poor residents suffered in silence.

Supreme Court, Round 2: Burwell v. Hobby Lobby (2014)

While the first Supreme Court decision was deemed a Democratic victory for upholding the ACA, notwithstanding the costly allowance for Medicaid hold-out states, the second Supreme Court ACA decision was a decisive Republican victory.

In 2012, several months after the NFIB v. Sebelius decision, David Green,an evangelical Christian and the founder and CEO of the successful chain of arts and crafts stores that operate under the brand Hobby Lobby, directed his company to file a lawsuit challenging ACA regulations requiring employer health plans to cover emergency contraceptives, such as the morning-after pill. The argument was that these requirements infringed on the company's religious freedom by forcing them to pay for contraception and abortions.

In 2014, the case was decided by the Supreme Court, with a 5-4 ruling in favor of the company and against the government. Writing for the Court, Justice Alito held that Hobby Lobby was not required to provide birth control access to employees under its sponsored health plan as the ACA would have required. The case established that for-profit corporations had the right to exemption from federal law based on religious beliefs.

While the practical implication of the Hobby Lobby decision was more limited than the NFIB v. Sebelius decision, it was nonetheless a potent symbolic victory for conservatives. Once again, the ACA had been painted as an imposition of liberal values and beaten back by conservatives.

Supreme Court, Round 3: King v. Burwell (2015)

The third Supreme Court decision on the ACA, King v. Burwell, looks different in the wake of the election of President-elect Trump and the prospect of ACA repeal. At the time, many observers (including the authors, for anyone who heard us speak on the subject) believed that the decision would put to rest, once and for all, the legality of the ACA. In retrospect, the scathing dissent by Justice Scalia stands out as another enduring piece of the case.

As described in Chapter 2, the ACA called upon the states to establish health insurance exchanges through which ACA-approved health plans would be sold to uncovered individuals, with sliding scale, income-based subsidies. The exchange-based policies were for people who earned too much to qualify for Medicaid, and were subject to the individual mandate to buy policies.

Nationally, roughly one third of the states and the District of Columbia responded to the ACA by setting up and running their own exchange marketplaces, but nearly twice as many states declined to set up exchanges. In some states, the federal government partnered with the state or offered other support for the state-specific exchange. But the solution for all states, particularly those Republican-led states that opted not to establish any exchange, was the federal healthcare.gov exchange. Through healthcare.gov, residents of all states could access ObamaCare insurance. (Residents of states that established exchanges are referred via web link to their own state's exchange website.)

The Republicans challenged healthcare.gov as an illegal exchange. Their argument was that the ACA never authorized the federal government to establish its own insurance exchange. Instead, the ACA directed the states to set up their own exchanges, and authorized HHS Secretary Sebelius to establish exchanges in any states that failed to do so. The specific terms of the law (Section 1401 of the ACA) authorized subsidies, in the form of tax credits, to be issued "through an Exchange established by the State." The IRS promulgated a regulation based on Section 1401 that defined the exchange as state-facilitated. Beginning in January 2014, the IRS began issuing subsidies through state exchanges, and also through healthcare.gov.

As in the NFIB v. Sebelius case, different lower courts ruled in conflicting ways on the issue. The question was whether the IRS definition of exchanges as state-facilitated precluded the subsequent broader definition of exchanges as state or federal. As a legal matter, the case turned on a highly technical case that is important to regulatory lawyers like us. The 1984 case, Chevron U.S.A., Inc. v. Natural Resources Defense Council, Inc. established that when a law delegates regulatory authority to an agency, the regulations are legal if they pass a two-part test. First, did Congress speak directly to the precise question at issue? Second, if not, is the statute silent or ambiguous on the issue? If the answer to the first question is no, and the answer to the second question is yes, then the agency's construction of the law is permissible.

Once again, Chief Justice Roberts wrote for the majority, holding that the clear intent of the ACA is to allow individuals to obtain subsidized insurance regardless of whether through state or federal exchange. Any other interpretation would kill the subsidies in a majority of states, undermining Congressional intent. In Roberts' words, "[i]t would be odd indeed for Congress to write such detailed instructions about . . . State Exchange, while having nothing to say about . . . a Federal Exchange."

As the ACA underwent its third Supreme Court review in three years, the subject of messy draftsmanship came up in both Roberts' opinion and the dissent. Chief Justice Roberts noted that "[t]he [ACA] contains more than a few examples of inartful drafting. Several features of the Act's passage contributed to that unfortunate reality. Congress wrote key parts of the Act behind closed doors, rather than through 'the traditional legislative process'... As a result, the Act does not reflect the type of care and deliberation that one might expect of such significant legislation." Nonetheless, Chief Justice Roberts found that "[t]he statutory scheme compels us to reject Petitioners' interpretation because it would destabilize the individual insurance market in any State with a Federal Exchange, and likely create the very 'death spirals' that Congress designed the Act to avoid." In short, the Court upheld the federal exchange because any other reading would lead to the illogical idea that Congress enabled the ACA to be torpedoed based on an obscure IRS provision.

Ultimately, Chief Justice Roberts summed up the King v.

Burwell decision in terms of judicial restraint: "In a democracy, the power to make the law rests with those chosen by the people. Our role is more confined – 'to say what the law is.' That is easier in some cases than in others. But in every case we must respect the role of the Legislature, and take care not to undo what it has done. A fair reading of legislation demands a fair understanding of the legislative plan. Congress passed the Affordable Care Act to improve health insurance markets, not to destroy them. If at all possible, we must interpret the Act in a way that is consistent with the former, and avoids the latter."

Once again, while he earned the respect of supporters of the ACA, Chief Justice Roberts was taken to task by its opponents for upholding the ACA. The opposition found its voice in the searing dissent of Justice Scalia, who memorably renamed the law. "We should start calling this law SCOTUScare," Justice Scalia declared. "[T]his Court's two decisions on the Act will surely be remembered through the years … And the cases will publish forever the discouraging truth that the Supreme Court of the United States favors some laws over others, and is prepared to do whatever it takes to uphold and assist its favorites."

Scalia's opposition centered on the literal meaning of the words of the ACA. He regarding the majority's decision as "jiggery-pokery" and "pure applesauce," which were nice ways of saying dishonest nonsense. If Section 1401 said an exchange "established by the State," then the only logical meaning was that only the states could establish an exchange, not the federal government. "Under all the usual rules of interpretation, in short, the Government should lose this case. But normal rules of interpretation seem always to yield to the overriding principle of the present Court: The Affordable Care Act must be saved."

Justice Scalia rejected the notion that the Supreme Court had the right to salvage a badly written law. "Perhaps sensing the dismal failure of its efforts to show that 'established by the State' means 'established by the State or the Federal Government,' the Court tries to palm off the pertinent statutory phrase as 'inartful drafting.' This Court, however, has no free-floating power 'to rescue Congress from its drafting errors.'" Scalia continued: "More importantly, the Court forgets that ours is a government of laws and not of men. That means we are governed by the terms of our laws, not by the unenacted will of our lawmakers."

Justice Scalia passed away in February 2016, leaving these words from 2015 as his legacy with respect to U.S. healthcare. The frustration he expressed about the ACA was shared by many, leading to the election of Donald Trump seven months later. As we'll explore in Chapter 4 and 5, Congressional Republicans and President Trump have a very different vision for U.S. healthcare. Repealing the ACA was at the top of their agenda. In the coming chapters, let's try to understand their alternative vision for U.S. healthcare.

FOUR:
A BETTER WAY? THE REPUBLICAN PLAN FOR U.S. HEALTHCARE

Long before Donald Trump emerged as the front-runner in the presidential campaign, congressional Republicans had formed alternative plans for U.S. healthcare. In fact, the current nominee for Secretary of the Department of Health and Human Services, Tom Price, had been the author of several bills reflecting these plans. Early in the summer of 2016, House Speaker Paul Ryan released the most comprehensive contemporary Republican agenda for healthcare under the banner of "A Better Way – Our Vision for a Confident America."

While other Republican leaders have distinct approaches – most notably Donald Trump, as we explore in Chapter 5 – Ryan's Better Way offers a useful starting point, a self-described "roadmap" to the Republican legislative vision. The real way to fix healthcare, argue Republicans, is smaller government, tax incentives, and market reforms.

Some of the Republican items sound like subtle repackaging, rather than complete rejections, of key ObamaCare components. In place of the individual mandate to buy insurance coverage, for example, Republicans propose tax credits for people who are uninsured to incentivize them to purchase insurance coverage on the individual market. In place of separate state insurance exchanges, Republicans propose to allow insurance companies to sell policies across state lines. To fund care for the most expensive patients with preexisting conditions, Republicans propose federal support for high-risk state insurance pools. On the surface, this doesn't sound hugely different from the ACA.

In other respects, however, the gap between the Republican vision and the ACA is so profound that it is difficult to imagine how ACA-driven changes to U.S. healthcare can be undone. One such area is the federal funding for Medicaid expansion to families at or near the federal poverty level (FPL). As detailed in Chapter 2, the Republican perspective is that the ACA expansion of government's role is a disaster.

In this chapter, we take a closer examination at the underlying assumptions that drive Republican policy, followed by a review of where the Better Way vision aligns and departs radically from the ACA and the current healthcare landscape, plus an analysis of the questions presented by the alternative Republican vision.

The Republican Imperative: Market-Driven Healthcare
The driving force behind Speaker Ryan's vision for U.S. healthcare is to "fix" healthcare in a way that does not add to the nation's tax burden. The most direct way to achieve this by utilizing a more market-driven system, where people pay for the healthcare they want and can afford. In the words of the Better Way, the goal is to "unleash[] the power of choice, and competition is the best way to lower healthcare costs and improve quality."

The Republican view harkens back to an era in which people bought the care they needed. The virtue of this system is price efficiency: healthcare providers charge what patients will pay, and supply and demand meet. It addresses the major weaknesses of our current system: the distortion and inflation in pricing caused when people other than the healthcare consumer (i.e., third-party payers like the government and insurance companies) foot the bill. A market-based system improves quality, as consumers vote with their wallets for the best providers.

> A market-based system improves quality, as consumers vote with their wallets for the best providers.

Implicit in this vision is the belief that the role of health insurance has gone too far. Insurance, in the Republican vision, was never meant to cover routine office visits, antibiotics, or birth control. Instead, the role of insurance is to cover infrequent, very expensive services, like treatment after an accident. An insurance that was only used in this narrow way would be affordable.

An analogy can be made to automobile insurance, which consumers only use for collisions, car theft, and other serious mishaps. If auto insurance also covered routine services, like oil changes, then the price of insurance would go up. In the Republican vision, patients can elect to buy up to a level of insurance that covers regular check-ups, but should be incentivized to pay out of pocket to drive market efficiency. As we'll explore ahead in this chapter, the model has its virtues in incentivizing market behavior, but also its limitations, when people cannot afford the care they need.

This aspect of the Republican vision is best exemplified by the promotion of a combination of model of Health Savings Account (HSA) and high-deductible health plans (HDHPs). HSAs are personal accounts through which individuals can pay their out-of-pocket expenses and keep funds that go unspent. HDHPs are similar to the major medical and catastrophic health plans of decades ago, where the insurance benefit set is limited and kicks in only in extreme events (e.g., a heart attack, stroke, or major accident) after the plan beneficiary has paid a deductible of $5,000 or $10,000.

The idea behind this form of coverage is that the HSA mechanism, through which consumers retain unspent money for routine expenses "helps patients understand the true cost of care, allows them to decide how much to spend, and provides them with the freedom to seek treatment at a place of their choosing."

HSAs and HDHPs have been around for years, but in the Republican plan, they shift from a disfavored, peripheral role to center stage. In 2016, for example, federal tax law limits HSAs to a maximum savings opportunity of $3,350 per person or $6,750 per family (an additional 1,000 for anyone over 55). Any distributions from the HSA for qualified out-of-pocket health expenses, such as insurance deductibles, prescription drugs, and bills not covered by insurance, such as vision and dental care) are fully tax deductible. The ACA limited HSAs, preventing them from being used for over-the-counter, non-prescription medications, and also increasing the excise penalty if funds are withdrawn for unqualified expense from 10% to 20%. Republicans also want to promote a cousin of HSAs, health reimbursement accounts (HRAs), in which employers provide a defined contribution amount and the employee must purchase coverage in private markets.

So if HSAs are already an option, what changes in a Republican vision? The bigger shift is the role of insurance. The Republican plan would do away with mandatory minimum essential benefit insurance coverage, which forces people into plans that cover everything, and promote narrower high deductible options. Under the ACA exchanges, consumers were presented with a confusing array of tiered plans, all of which covered routine care and other minimum essential benefits. The only allowances for catastrophic plans with narrower coverage under the ACA were for people under 30 and people with a "hardship exemption" such as being homeless or a victim of domestic violence.

ACA Plan Type	Actuarial Value	Typical Deductible	Typical Coinsurance	Out-of-Pocket Max
Bronze	60%	$5,000	30%	$6,350
Silver	70%	$2,000	20%	$6,350
Gold	80%	-	20%	$6,350
Platinum	90%	-	10%	$6,350
Catastrophic	N/A	$6,350	0%	$6,350

In the Republican vision, catastrophic plans offer a "LC/LB" – Low Cost/Low Benefit option. They are in place to manage a disaster, but individuals pay directly out-of-pocket – with employer-provided or personal funds – for all other healthcare costs. Patients, in turn, will demand price transparency and vote with their wallets for the healthcare providers who deliver it.

Strengthening the Medicare Advantage (MA) HMO program

As a way of advancing the power of market economics, an overarching Republican priority is privatization. The clearest example of this preference is Medicare Advantage (MA), also known as Medicare Part C.

Since 1997, Medicare has offered beneficiaries the option of receiving their Medicare benefits through a private health plan, instead of on a straight fee-for-service basis. Originally called "Medicare+Choice," the program was renamed Medicare Advantage in 2003. For beneficiaries, MA offers the ease of getting all services through an organized healthcare system, setting their own additional premium charges to beneficiaries. The MA plans, in turn, accept risk from CMS and earn their profits based on their success in managing the delivery of care efficiently.

MA plans have been popular with Medicare beneficiaries, growing from 13% of all Medicare enrollment in 2003 to over 30% today. Republicans embrace MA as a privatized option that features managed care characteristics. It offers patients the ability to decide which plans they want to participate in, increasing market competition. The MA plans themselves are incentivized to deliver high quality care as efficiently as possible, reducing the role of government.

As we'll return to in Chapter 10, it is not difficult to imagine strong Republican support for shifting all federal health funding over time to privatized care administration and delivery. The Republicans praise Medicare Part D prescription drug coverage as a privatized model as well. By contrast, Republicans complain that fee-for-service Medicare has confusing deductibles, inconsistent patient responsibility provisions, and masks the true cost of healthcare from beneficiaries.

The long-term Republican vision is for Medicare to become a market-based competitively bid program, generally known in Washington as a "premium support" design. Variations of this proposal have surfaced over decades. In broad terms, the government would foster the creation of a Medicare Exchange market for insurance plans that would initially compete for customers against regular Medicare. The insurance plans would compete on cost and cost sharing. The government would offset the costs of the plans by payments to the plans on behalf of enrolled seniors. Sicker seniors would receive higher offset payments, as would lower income seniors. High income seniors would bear a larger share of plan costs.

While a bigger move to privatization remains on the Republican wish list for now (and will require a sales effort to America's seniors), in the near-term, the focus is on promoting and strengthening the already popular MA, based on its alignment with Republican values.

The ACA set MA benchmark caps that limited the value-based enhancement payments, rather than allowing them to be tied to fee-for-service rates. Republicans advocate differentiating reimbursement as a way to foster competition and reward quality care. Similarly, Republicans approach would reduce CMS governmental authority to reduce payments to MA plans based on patient health.

Finally, Republicans also propose changes to MA to

empower beneficiaries and make them better healthcare shoppers. Current regulations require MA plans to offer the same benefit set to all MA beneficiaries. Republicans want to free plans to encourage seniors to choose "high value" benefits, but forgo "low value" benefits or unnecessary services – a parallel to the goal of HSA/HDHP plans in the private insurance context. Presumably, MA monthly reimbursement to the Plan would be adjusted to the level of services elected by each beneficiary. Republicans also propose an annual three-month "switching period" for seniors who elect a new plan, only to find that one or more of their physicians were not providers for their new plan. MA previously allowed this, but the ACA removed this flexibility and locked seniors into their choices made in the late Fall open enrollment period.

Encouraging Market Forces Through Deregulation

Hand in hand with privatization, deregulation is a banner that the Republicans have long waved. The Republican passion for low-cost solutions to healthcare focuses on ways to improve the forces of market efficiency beyond patient behavior through deregulation. While the Better Way embraces the traditional Republican philosophy in favor of a diminished federal role and increased power at the state level to make choices relevant to the local market, the theme of deregulation offers new power to insurance companies and to employers.

> The Republican passion for low-cost solutions to healthcare focuses on ways to improve the forces of market efficiency beyond patient behavior through deregulation.

At the same time that Republicans would slim down the role

of insurers through high-deductible, catastrophic plans, they also look to enable health insurance companies to compete more freely in a national market (regulated federally in place of the current state-by-state regulation). Reducing regulation also extends to reducing the constraints of healthcare-specific taxes, such as the 2.3% tax on medical devices imposed as part of the ACA compromise.

In the Republican vision, these regulatory and tax impositions on private industry not only distort prices, but destroy jobs. The Better Way plan alludes to doing away with the removal of the McCarran-Ferguson Act antitrust protection for insurance companies, which would allow for unregulated competition. Republicans not only want to let insurance companies compete nationally, but also to enable consumers to purchase plans registered in other states, and to give states the ability to enter into compacts for interstate pooling (presumably for a single plan being offered in several states simultaneously).

One interesting deregulation proposal inside the "Better Way" plan relates to empowering physicians to own hospitals. In 2010, Medicare regulations enacted a prohibition of physician-owned hospitals. The criticism leading up to that change was that it enabled physicians to profit from their own referral streams and also allowing them to cherry pick and carve outs of more lucrative subsets of specialty services (such as surgical specialties) from general acute care hospitals. The Ryan plan proposes to once again allow physicians to own hospitals, claiming that this will stimulate competition and lower healthcare costs.

Deregulating Employers

The Republican plan also looks to open up options for employers. In place of the mandate to require insurance which constrained options, employers would have the choice to provide insurance or not. They would also have greater flexibility to self-insure, avoiding the insurance market entirely by paying directly for employee healthcare costs, combined with stop-loss insurance against large claims. The Republican plan hints at federal regulation of stop-loss insurance purchases by self-insured employers, a policy that would reverse Obama administration positions in the name of greater flexibility and increased choice for small businesses.

Self-insurance is already a popular option for large employers under the Employee Retirement Income Security Act (ERISA), but Republicans are interested in promoting more self-insurance. The Ryan plan advocates employer incentive discounts on employees' health insurance for participation in prevention and wellness programs, while also insulating these programs from current claims by the U.S. Equal Employment Opportunity Commission (EEOC) that such programs may violate the Americans with Disabilities Act or the Genetic Information Nondiscrimination Act.

For smaller employers, Republicans hold out the option of "Association Health Plans" – allowing small businesses and other organizations to band together for the purpose of purchasing a single health plan. This policy is supposed to lower overhead costs for individual businesses and lower plan costs through increased bargaining power of the group of smaller entities. The policy also mentions the possibility of allowing pooling by individuals in "individual health pools" (IHPs) without providing details about how individuals would become eligible for participation in IHPs or what mechanism would prompt insurers to deal with such entities. Both of these types of pools would have to comply with rules against "cherry picking" only healthy participants or charging higher premiums for sicker or high risk patients.

An interesting wrinkle in the Better Way plan is its "preserving employer-sponsored insurance plans" initiative. While the name might sound innocuous, the real focus is tax reform. The plan criticizes the current IRS tax code treatment of employer-provided healthcare as an unlimited tax deduction, positing that this has had a negative impact on employee wages. Republicans argue that, by capping the employer health insurance deduction, the government will raise money from overly generous plans and cause employers to buy less health insurance with their employees. Ironically, this parallels perhaps the single most unpopular part of the ACA vision: the so-called "Cadillac" tax on rich employee benefit plans that drew howls from Republicans and more conservative Democrats as well. Republicans assert that less employer-provided insurance would be a good thing, citing a report that the employers, as a whole, spend an additional 10 to 15% on more extensive coverage because the exclusion is uncapped. Imposing a cap would encourage insurance companies to scale back plans, reducing premiums and increasing take-home pay.

Medical Liability (Tort) Reform

In addition to deregulating, the Republican plan takes on a historical target: trial lawyers. The "Better Way" plan advocates national caps on noneconomic damages in malpractice cases and limitations on lawyers' contingency fees. It cites the examples of Texas and California, which imposed these reforms on the state level, with relatively positive results in controlling medical liability insurance premiums and in attracting hard-hit practice areas like obstetric medicine. The policy also encourages additional policy expansion by the states, with mention of the potential for national legislation that would enact safe harbors for practitioners following clinical practice guidelines established by their respective medical societies.

Insurance Reforms

If the foregoing aspects of the Better Way healthcare plan had a distinctive Republican "feel" in the orientation towards market-driven solutions, the Republican plan also has its own set of assurances – overlapping with integral ObamaCare reforms – to ease voter anxiety. The focus is on "common sense" areas like historic insurance practices (that consumers disliked) that preserve fairness and individual liberty. Although Republicans are trying to reclaim these ideas, the bottom line is they align with things that are popular with all voters:

Pre-existing Conditions. Republicans support the popular ACA reform of requiring insurance companies to underwrite patients regardless of pre-existing health conditions.

Coverage for Adult Children. Republicans would continue the current ObamaCare requirement to allow dependent children to stay on parents' health plans through age 26.

Ending Lifetime Caps. Republicans support regulations that would eliminate lifetime benefit caps from health insurance plans.

Cancellation Protection. Republicans support for regulations to prevent cancellation or nonrenewal of insurance policies when a beneficiary becomes ill.

Continuous Coverage Protections. The Republican plan proposes to extend the continuous coverage regulation of the employer-sponsored plan market to the individual plan market.

Fair Premium. Traditionally, the age-banding of policies had been 5 to 1, meaning that policyholders at age 64 could not be charged more than 5 times the premium a 21 year old beneficiary could be charged. The ACA required it to not exceed 3 to 1. The proposed regulation would set a federal guideline of 5 to 1, although the states have regulatory authority to vary the ratio.

State Innovation Grants. This regulatory proposal would revive a 2009 Republican initiative to offer states, collectively, $25 billion to address insurance market structures, with awards on a sliding scale according for premium reduction and other cost-shifting performance standards.

High Risk Pools. The plan advocates "robust" high risk pools supported by $25 billion in annual Federal support. The pools would have premium caps and wait lists would be prohibited. The federal and state governments would cooperate to assure actuarial solvency.

Open Enrollment. The plan proposes a one-time open-enrollment period as almost a one-time amnesty for uninsured to come into the market or for insured to switch between markets. At one time all potential subscribers would be offered the same choices (presumably in state-controlled individual plan markets). Those who do not enroll would still be able to buy coverage later on, but would forfeit continuous coverage protections and be subject to higher premiums.

Conscience Protections. As in most Republican legislation, the plan contains conscience protections and strong antiabortion regulations. (In contrast to the other items on this list, this particular provision is popular religious and social conservatives, rather than the broader public.)

Tax Credits to Make Coverage Portable
One of the Republican centerpieces is a shift to a "universal advanceable, refundable tax credit" that will enable coverage portability, providing "every American access to financial support for an insurance plan chosen by the individual and can be taken with them job to job, home to start a small business or raise a family, and even into retirement years."

As a practical matter, the tax credit would only be available to people who did not have access to an employer-sponsored plan, Medicare, or Medicaid. The credit would take the form of a monthly advance payment that the taxpayer would use to purchase regular private health insurance coverage through a system regulated by the states. Taxpayers receiving the credits would receive a fixed monthly amount adjusted for age, not tied to the actual costs of health insurance, but "large enough to purchase the typical pre-ObamaCare health plan." If they did not use the whole amount, the remaining funds would be deposited in an HSA and could be used for other healthcare costs at the individual's discretion.

Washing the Federal Government's Hands of Medicaid
As noted above, Medicaid has been the most politically divisive part of the U.S. healthcare system since its 1965 inception, with enduring Republican misgivings about it. This Republican critique laments that it is the single largest U.S. healthcare program ($545 billion annual expenditures by both federal and state governments), and - left to weaker state law enforcement resources - particularly vulnerable to

fraud and abuse.

Republican complaints about Medicaid go beyond the expense and taxpayer burden to a claim that it reduced access to care and cut payments to physicians, putting additional stress on hospital ERs that are required to see patients and that already serve millions of patients for whom no primary care access is readily available (and increases the EMTALA cost-shifting as previously discussed).

The Republican reform proposal is to transfer more responsibility to the states, allowing them to elect either a per capita allotment or a block grant funding mechanism. Under the per capita allotment, the total federal funding would be reduced some 20% over time, and would not allow states to obtain more federal matching dollars merely by spending more state dollars.

States would be the primary and virtually sole administrator of Medicaid under block grant funding. Using an allotment based on 2016 expenditures, states would draw matching monies down from the federal government starting in 2019, and thereafter use the set per capita formula. States would no longer be able to expand their Medicaid programs and, over time, payments for (and presumably state coverage of) able bodied adults would be phased out, and Medicaid dollars from the block grants would be shifted to the other three categories (i.e., aged, blind-disabled, and pregnant women-children).

In the Republican vision, the federal government would pull back from Medicaid program management and there would be little state/federal interaction and no federal approval process for waivers and other programs. These reforms offer the states the benefit of flexibility, through the per capita allotment program to enact reforms such as requiring able-bodied adults to be searching for work or in training programs to maintain eligibility, and the freedom to update waivers as long as the waiver program proposed was budget neutral to the federal government.

A Gentler Approach to Medicare?

In contrast to the Republican downsizing of Medicaid, the Republicans assert a desire to strengthen a Medicare program weakened by ObamaCare. Unwilling to be critical of a plan as popular with seniors as Medicare, Republicans only hint at what is actually a deep and profound concern for them: an unsustainable rate of Medicare expenditure.

One immediate step to reduce costs is the Republican goal to raise the Medicare eligibility age to match Social Security. Currently, people aged 65 or older can select Medicare coverage, while the "normal" retirement age for Social Security has been pushed up to 67. The Republicans propose to move the Medicare eligibility age up starting in 2020, and moving it gradually thereafter until it is matches the Social Security retirement age.

Other Medicare Reforms

Medigap Reform. The Republican plan cites a study that shows beneficiaries with MediGap insurance spend 33% more on healthcare than those without MediGap insurance. They find this to be a misdirected incentive and propose phasing MediGap out, with an initial reduction in 2020 to allow MediGap to cover only half of the out-of-pocket limits and deductibles.

Combining Medicare Parts A and B. The difference in the deductibles and co-pays between Parts A and B would be eliminated through a unified deductible and a streamlined

Medicare Savings Plan, reducing patient out of pocket costs. This change would also save money by instituting uniform 20% cost sharing for all physician and hospital services in a combined Part A and Part B. This would amount to a substantial savings to the program as a 20% cost sharing for hospital services would be significantly higher than the current phased co-insurance structure. The combination of Parts A and B would place Medicare Fee-for-Service on par with the structure of MA.

Protecting the Doctor-Patient Relationship. The plan makes non-specific complaints about how regulation intrudes on the doctor-patient relationship, and promises to reform the laws to strengthen the doctor-patient relationship. It cites restrictions on the ability of physicians to offer non-covered services and proposes regulations that would allow physicians and patients to agree upon services outside of the Medicare system. The plan also champions physician choice in determining which health plans to join.

Uncompensated Care Reform. The Republicans propose deferring the scheduled cuts to disproportionate share funding scheduled for 2018 and 2019, and order the HHS Secretary to design a new uncompensated care reimbursement program for hospitals to be implemented in 2020, thereby avoiding any DSH cuts prior to the implementation of a new plan.

Medicare Compare. The plan proposes to establish a quality and outcome comparison set of measures for Medicare Fee-for-Service, and starting in 2021, HHS will publish a comparison of all MA and FFS in a given Metropolitan Statistical Area (MSA). The ACA national quality initiatives would be replaced by Medicare Compare.

Demolishing the ObamaCare Innovation Entities

As noted in Chapter 3, the Republicans saved their most contempt for the Obama Administration entities created to review and streamline healthcare decision-making and spending. These show up in the "Better Way" plan in the form of plans to defund the Independent Payment Advisory Board (IPAB) and Center for Medicare and Medicaid Innovation (CMMI).

A Republican Vision of Healthcare Innovation

In "Promoting Innovation in Health Care," the Ryan plan addresses what the Republicans see as regulatory hurdles to allowing better collaboration among researchers in finding cures for many diseases. Most of the regulatory reform is directed at streamlining the FDA and how it processes clinical trial data, but the proposals also include eliminating review of smartphone apps as medical devices, promoting personalized medicine through biomarkers, incentivizing off-label use of approved drugs, and using "big data" to fast track reviews. Innovation also includes streamlining of medical record regulations and improving meaningful use requirements.

Assessing the Ryan Vision of U.S. Healthcare: Taking on Straw Men

Where does the Republican vision articulated by Speaker Ryan make sense and where it is off-base? In some places, Republicans offer promising ideas. In other places, they are taking shots not at ObamaCare, but a Republican bogeyman – single payer/universal healthcare.

The most disappointing thing about the Republican plan is the way that it doesn't take ObamaCare seriously, but instead attacks and belittles a strawman version, arguing that "it makes no sense for one federal agency to dictate the

contents of every American's health insurance plan."
ObamaCare, of course, did no such thing. What the
Republican plan takes aim at is the fear of support for
universal Medicare of the kind that candidate Bernie
Sanders advocated during the presidential campaign. As we
discuss in Chapter 10, the failure of the Clinton campaign
has sent Democrats back to the drawing board to consider
what their healthcare vision will be. One likely outcome is
increasing Democratic support for a more Progressive
alternative, such as universal Medicare. But the report
mischaracterizes the ACA by suggesting that this is what the
last six years have wrought.

The Ryan vision is replete with other strawmen and
apocrypha. When sources are examined, it is short on hard
facts, makes illogical leaps to make points, and is based
heavily on political opinion. For instance, one discussion
starts: "Part of the reason this may be happening" without
giving specifics.

Tax Impact as the Driving Imperative
Despite the sometimes flimsy economic analysis
underpinning the policy recommendations, the strawman
platitudes have a very firm and consistent message:
Republicans will support federal legislation that isn't
universal Medicare and which do not add to the nation's
tax burden.

> Republicans will support federal legislation
> that isn't universal Medicare and which do not
> add to the nation's tax burden.

These appear to be the essential criteria for legislation, and
the reasons the "headline titles" vary considerably in some

cases from the actual policy discussed.

As noted at the beginning of this chapter, the Ryan plan boils down to a tax reform document, where the tax reform proposals just happen to touch on healthcare issues. Assessments of what legislation will be pushed forward and its impact on the American healthcare system that follow all must start from the premise that all new bills must pass a Republican litmus test on taxation. If the ObamaCare provision at issue can be called a "'tax," then that provision must be repealed. If there is a change to the tax code that benefits small businesses or assists the government, then the law should be enacted.

Viewed through the looking glass of Republican anti-tax, anti-government expansion principles, the Republican policy recommendations are consistent. Even the perceived negative effects of ObamaCare, while largely not factual, are legitimate philosophical objections consistent with existing Republican tenets. This is the overriding lesson of reviewing the stated Ryan critiques of ObamaCare. But the basic divide on the issues run deeper – Republicans do not support the insurance model in healthcare.

Republican Plans and Basic Premises of Insurance
The overriding reason for any kind of insurance is to socialize risk. In the usual sequence, insureds pay premiums to insurers in return for promises to pay in the occurrence of a chance event. The idea is to concentrate resources with stewards who will manage financial assets to assure that funding will be available if and when one of the chance events occurs.

In such a structure, all insureds pay a small piece of the total cost, and yet get the full benefit of financial protection in the event one of the chance events insured against befalls them individually. (For you younger readers, this is essentially an ancient form of crowdfunding). The insurer takes on the risk that the premiums they collect plus the returns of the financial assets they manage will exceed the costs of the payouts to insureds suffering the chance events.

The problem with this concept is that it is really not applied to healthcare in the US. (In many states, the health insurers do not call health insurance "insurance" – referring to them only as benefit plans). Insurers of all kinds – including the federal government – have been trying to dump their risk onto the backs of providers, employers, and beneficiaries for decades.

Insurance company risk-shifting techniques include (1) capitation payments, (2) caps and limits on coverage, (3) selling third-party administrator (TPA) services for "self-insured" plans, (4) per-incidence of health event flat payments (like DRGs for hospitals under Medicare), and (5) routine denial of otherwise covered claims to raise the costs of collection. So-called "Plan Design" visits beneficiaries with an ever-increasing share of the costs of healthcare by restricting benefits (limiting the "chance events" that the insurer will pay on, and leaving the beneficiaries to pay the shortfall) and by inserting more "co-pays, premium costs, and co-insurance" to be paid directly by beneficiaries. These actions, of course, run directly contrary to the first tenet of insurance: to socialize risk.

To its credit, ObamaCare (and certainly Bernie Sanders' Universal Medicare) tried to socialize risk, by including more people in insurance pools, by mandating minimum benefits for the plans, by mandating participation, and by subsidizing premium costs for people who couldn't afford it. All of this socialization of the costs of healthcare is really not a political choice in the first instance – in a normative sense, it is simply being true to the first principle of insurance to socialize the risk. If we were addressing true insurance, we would support the concept of universal inclusion and socializing risk. Since we cannot control to a large extent upon whom the worst of healthcare issues is going to visit, everyone contributes a little bit and agrees to pay for what befalls the unlucky one.

But healthcare is expensive, and many people want to make value judgments on who should and should not receive the benefits of health coverage. We would all agree to pitch in and pay for the mother of three who landed in the ER after her minivan was hit by a drunk driver. None of us are wild about paying the bill for the drunk that caused the accident. Does your opinion change if it turns out the drunk turned to liquor in distress because his wife, the driver of the minivan, had an affair with a neighbor?

Our existing health insurance programs do not work that way. We have not embraced socializing risk. We do not require it of insurers. Mandates seem to be an anathema to Republicans, as some sort of restriction on freedom. In fairness, ObamaCare mandates were not designed to restrict freedom; they were designed to address fairness in socializing risk. Why should someone "free ride" and not buy any insurance, get in a car accident, and expect insurance to pay any of the costs of their healthcare? It isn't their fault for getting in the accident, but to bear no financial responsibility, even their relative small premium costs, seems wrong, since the hospital will have to cover those costs, and pass those expenses on to the rest of us who are buying insurance through raising the rates we have to pay.

Mandates are just an example of how Republicans do not

support the insurance model for healthcare. Instead, Republicans see the tax code and the capital markets as the model for healthcare. The tax code serves as an allocation mechanism, to provide for some financial incentive to gain and maintain health insurance, but not including penalties for anyone who doesn't participate. And the capital markets drive companies and the government to avoid risk. So Republican measures, including virtually all of the suggestions put forth in the Ryan plan, focus on tax code redesign to support (some) individuals to pay for their healthcare through tax credits or deductions, and trust the capital markets to allocate healthcare resources efficiently.

Towards Pricing Efficiency

The counter-argument is that Republican plan's aversion to the insurance model does have one upside. We don't call the insurance company because a refrigerator breaks down; we call a repairman. So why does our system (both before and even more so after the ACA) enshrine insurance for routine regular non-catastrophic care? The insinuation of insurers into the market of patients needing more regular types of healthcare and healthcare providers offering that care translates into higher prices for consumers and less profits for providers.

Imagine if every time you went to the supermarket, there was a 30% or so tax for a middleman to evaluate if you chose the right food and to make sure the store delivered it well. Identifying as large a segment of the healthcare marketplace as possible from which insurance could be removed would be the best way to drive more efficient pricing.

Similarly, the Republican proposal to increase out-of-pocket spending through HSAs and HDHPs has promise in driving towards more efficient healthcare pricing. Table 14 highlights the historical interrelationship between third-party payment and out-of-pocket spending. Over the past five decades, government spending on healthcare has soared, while out-of-pocket spending has plummeted. Rising healthcare costs in this time period can be explained both by third-party payer insensitivity to price increases and to patient indifference to pricing when without "skin in the game."

Table 14

The Inverse Relationship Between Out-of-pocket and Government Healthcare Spending, 1960s-2010s

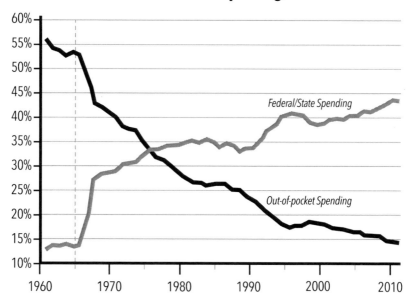

NOTE: Vertical dotted line indicates creation of Medicare and Medicaid in 1965.
Source: Centers for Medicare and Medicaid Services

Flimsy Economic Analysis

Not all of the analysis in the Republican plan is sound. Especially illustrative of this point is the discussion on the "tax benefit" of having employers' contributions to healthcare plans excluded from the ordinary income of employees. First of all, the common employee's understanding of benefits is that these are perks, not wages, paid for by the employer, and not generally includible in employee's pay stubs. Nevertheless, many "benefits" are monetized and imputed as income to employees, or, under the Internal Revenue Code (IRC), excluded as taxable income (e.g., matching 401k contributions by employers). Tax policy wonks view the world differently, and see all benefits as taxable, and view the exclusion of employer-paid healthcare benefits as a gigantic government give-away. They believe that a rightly enforced tax code would in fact include all of these employer expenses for benefits as income for employees.

The tax code is so byzantine that most economists would agree that it is not accurate to describe the impact of the existing practice as a gigantic government giveaway, but rather as a sensible practice of encouraging employers to treat workers better economically in non-wage terms. Employers benefit by having a healthier work force, even though the healthcare benefits the individuals directly, and the employer only indirectly.

Economists would agree that payments to employees are taxable as wages, and expenses of running the business are deductions for employers. But attributing an expense to an employee as a benefit can be difficult, even for economists. For instance, what about tools that can be used at work, but also off-the-clock, such as an employee car. Is any portion of the car expense includible in the employee's income? There are complicated rules where the tax code does try to attribute the car as income to certain employees in certain situations. There are even more complicated rules for the inverse situation where the employee owns the car and bears the expense of ownership in the first instance, but deploys the personal car on behalf of the business. Logically, Ryan proposes simplifying the IRC to include everything paid on the employee's behalf as wages. He makes a concession in this instance, at least in the intermediate term, by proposing to even the deduction playing field between employees receiving healthcare insurance at work and those buying it on the insurance markets.

Regardless of the debatable tax policy, the plan goes further and makes an illogical leap from economics to baseless rhetoric. The Republican plan argues that by capping the employer contribution exclusion, and taxing the excess at some level, all sorts of faerie dust will shower on Americans. The plan actually states that employers will reduce their contributions to healthcare insurance purchases and move the money saved to higher wages for employees. This just won't happen; employers will reduce contributions to healthcare benefits to avoid any above-the-cap tax that Republicans might impose, and will not pass the excess (the reduction of contributions) on as wages.

> *The Republican plan argues that by capping the employer contribution exclusion, and taxing the excess at some level, all sorts of faerie dust will shower on Americans.*

The Ryan plan even goes on to argue inconsistently that even though hardly anyone will be subject to the tax (meaning that there will be very little employer expense reduction), the cap on the exclusion will raise everyone's take home pay. With what? Money just printed by the employers?

If the cap is set high enough that most all (and eventually all) plans will be purchased by employers at or under the cap, then there will be no dollars available to be shifted anywhere. Wages will not go up as a result.

Worse, insurance plans won't care about the caps. They will charge premiums that the market will bear. Who is going to pay the above-the-cap premiums? The employees of course. The far more likely scenario emanating from a cap on employer's deduction for healthcare benefit expense is that (1) employers will benefit from the cap, (2) insurers will keep making their cost increases going forward, and (3) employees will pay an increasing share of the plan cost, thereby reducing their disposable income. There will be absolutely no gain in take home wages as the plan argues.

Net Expensive for Taxpayers

The "Better Way" proposals illustrate House Speaker Ryan's self-perceived principal role as protector of the U.S. budget. When it comes to healthcare, this translates to shifting costs away from the federal government and onto others, primarily state governments and individuals. For instance, the promotion of HSAs overtly incentivizes people to put more of their own money aside so that others don't have to pay for their healthcare. Even the tax credit strategy will increase the costs for Americans as a whole.

As we discuss in Chapter 7, the types of health plans that will be affordable through the use of tax credits will be very limited in coverage, leaving either the taxpayer to make up the shortfall of the costs of care, or, in the case of hospitalization, leaving the hospital to shift its expense onto the backs of ratepayers of more comprehensive employer-sponsored insurance. Moreover, the verification process tentatively described will exclude many people from obtaining tax credits in the first place.

"For All Americans": Fool's Gold?

The headline message of the Better way plan also includes an undertone of universality - several of the proposals repeat the words "for all Americans." At some level, Republicans believe this to be true: the tax code reaches all Americans, so anything done in the tax code impacts healthcare is a policy for all Americans. But we should not confuse the Republican sense that the tax code is applicable to all Americans as some form of universal healthcare, despite what the conservative news outlet spinners might say.

First, only taxpayers will be the direct objects of the Republican policy. For people and matters that are beyond the reach of the tax code, there will be no impact of the Ryan proposals (beyond the impact of the repeal of ObamaCare). For example, undocumented aliens will be left to forego healthcare, receive it underground, or seek care in the local ER (which has to stabilize them under EMTALA).

Second, verification procedures will limit tax credit awards, and not every American will qualify for them, even if they are income qualified.

Third, without mandates, many Americans will self-select out of either government tax credits or using the credit to buy low cost/limited benefit health plans and risk high financial burdens if they have a health crisis.

Fourth, and most critically, the envisioned tax code revisions do nothing on the basic access issues; no additional doctors are being hired and no additional services are being provided. Under the Republican plan, individuals are left to navigate the tax code and the capital markets to try to anticipate and offset healthcare costs, and buy their healthcare wherever the markets make resources available.

> Under the Republican plan, individuals are left to navigate the tax code and the capital markets to try to anticipate and offset healthcare costs, and buy their healthcare wherever the markets make resources available.

Positive Market-Driven Reforms Outweighed by Financial Burden Unreality

For those looking for the "good news" in Speaker Ryan's plan, the encouragement of more market-driven pricing and empowerment of patients to be better consumers of healthcare are positive things. While the ACA and other federal reforms have taken aim at the lack of pricing transparency, there remains a distortion in healthcare pricing that the Republican reforms seek to correct. This would be good news in creating more clarity and efficiency in the system.

The challenge, however, is that it is wishful thinking to think that pricing corrections and turning patients into better consumers are going to address the staggering costs of healthcare for those with chronic conditions or catastrophic needs. We can't get the majority of the American public to eat right, exercise, or otherwise look after their health, and many millions smoke and make other poor choices in regard to their health. The idea that they are going to become super-intelligent consumers of healthcare overnight is pure fantasy.

In the meantime, the Republican plan turns a blind eye to the human costs for those who are struggling to make ends meet and have no wherewithal to assume unexpected healthcare costs. Republican suspicion that Medicaid is going to be so great that it will incentivize people not to work defies reality. As we discuss in Chapter 7, while many reforms of the Medicaid program are appropriate, stripping people of eligibility (or keeping people in hold-out states without coverage) is a disaster and a potential serious national threat in the event of some kind of pandemic.

FIVE:
THE TRUMP WILD CARD

ObamaCare. We're going to repeal it, we're going to replace it, get something great. Repeal it, replace it, get something great![4]

While the "Better Way" plan spelled out the Republican vision for healthcare in detail, Donald Trump's own personal vision is harder to pin down. On the campaign trail, Trump repeatedly talked about replacing ObamaCare with "something terrific" but offered relatively few hints of what he wanted to do beyond repealing ObamaCare.

In this chapter, we examine those hints, with an eye to the question of how much of a gap exists between the Republican (i.e., Ryan) vision spelled out in Chapter 4 and Trump's own ideas. One challenge in answering this question is that, in several cases, President-elect Trump appears to be have spoken on both sides of the same issue.

President-elect Trump appears to be have spoken on both sides of the same issue.

After differentiating a "Trumpian" vision for healthcare, we turn to the question of whether Trump is likely to insert himself and his own distinctly populist views. Will President Trump exercise the power of social media by tweeting and mustering public support whenever he departs from Republican orthodoxies? Alternatively, will he delegate healthcare policy to the experts around him? If so, what are they likely to do?

Answering these questions inherently involves a degree of speculation, not only because of inconsistencies in Donald Trump's own personal statements, but also based on anticipated conflict beginning when the 115th Congress reconvenes in January 2017 under the leadership of House Speaker Paul Ryan and Senate Majority Leader Mitch McConnell. Many people expect a Republican three-headed monster: the populist President Trump focused on making good on commitments to supporters, the more cost-conscious, tax- and budget-focused, and religiously motivated House under Speaker Ryan's leadership, and the more narrowly divided Senate offering a slightly more socially conscious and liberal perspective.

Finally, we attempt to understand the issue of the Trump scare factor as it relates to healthcare. In the wake of the unexpected election results, hundreds of thousands of people took to the streets to protest the coming administration. While calmer pundits trumpeted that "Trump is no Washington" and focused on the practical questions ahead, many continue to fear a chief executive whose volatility and inconsistent pronouncements have played into the campaign critique that he was temperamentally unfit to serve as President.

Candidate Trump's Healthcare Vision
As the 2016 presidential campaign unfolded, Donald Trump joined other Republican candidates in promising to repeal

the ACA. There was relatively little suggestion of what to replace it with. Donald Trump was no exception. This may be a reflection of how complicated healthcare can be. Like other Republicans, he followed a nonspecific line, starting with the basic premise that market forces, rather than government policies, should determine how healthcare is provided.

On the campaign trail, Trump ran as a populist, railing against government control over people's lives and promising to hold companies accountable for their economic decisions. His command of the issues was not always firm. He took five different positions on abortion over a three-day period in February 2016. His evaluations of programs rested on whether or not they were "good deals" for the American people. At one point, he claimed that his employees were having a "tremendous problem" with ObamaCare when in fact they were covered by his company.[5]

Several other moments of divergence from Republican dogma stand out. In February 2016, Donald Trump praised the ACA individual mandate and then was forced to flip-flop the next day, promising to repeal all of the ACA, including the mandate, as soon as he was elected.[6] While this may have been a mistake, it is interesting to note his remarks, including during one of the primary debates, where he startled the Republican panel when he expressed support for a single-payer system. He noted that it worked well in Canada and Scotland, although his preference was for a private system, rather than one administered by the government.[7]

Trump's independence also showed at a campaign rally in January, when he took a page out of his Democratic opponent's messaging, lambasting the pharmaceutical industry for drug pricing and promising that he would save $300 billion a year by negotiating drug prices for Medicare and propose laws to allow Americans to buy drugs from other countries.[8]

These statements leave little room for doubt that there is "daylight" between Trump's own views and the Republican plan. At the same time, Trump eventually proposed a seven point proposal for healthcare reform that echoes the "Better Way" approach. The Trump plan begins with a full repeal of ObamaCare, placing responsibility for the replacement with Congress, and outlining a few suggestions as "a place to start."

Most of the proposals were consistent with the Republican party line, including the need to do away with the mandate, allow insurance companies to compete in multiple states, fund Medicaid through block grants to states, and change the way health insurance is taxed. Trump broke with the GOP by proposing to allow Americans to import drugs from overseas as a way to deal with drug pricing, claiming that this private industry provides a public service that should be open to the free market.

Clues in Trump's History

Can we find clues to Donald Trump's healthcare vision in his pre-presidential campaign history? A review of his earlier statements on healthcare, as in other areas, reflects politics that are mixed, neither classically Democratic or Republican. He was a registered Democrat for most of his adult life. While the early indications are that he has assembled an administration that will govern from the Right, Healthcare appears to be one place where Trump may be motivated to assert a less ideological, more populist perspective.

Healthcare appears to be one place where Trump may be motivated to assert a less ideological, more populist perspective.

For those worried readers who question Trump's capacity to advocate rationally on healthcare policy (or any other areas of governance), it may be useful to remember that he is hardly the first chief executive to be targeted for such criticism. The nearest recent analog would seem to be Ronald Reagan – someone seen as a relative lightweight by media elites, and despite being a two-term California governor, someone seen as having little experience that would translate into being able to run the country. Many people were disenchanted with Reagan as a "mere actor" and many of those people were Republicans.

To be sure, Trump's public persona can be off-putting. He is self-absorbed and displays more than the usual CEO-like egocentric behaviors. These are well cemented in the American public's perception, with over a decade of television exposure and decades of tabloid coverage documenting his behaviors.

At the same time, Trump has an Ivy League degree. He is very knowledgeable about his core construction, hotel, golf course development, financing, and real estate operations. And he is not the first somewhat eccentric personality to be elected President. George Washington himself wore his homemade general officer's uniform to sessions of the Continental Congress before being appointed head of the Continental Army. Abraham Lincoln, a successful railroad lawyer, has been identified in recent years as a bipolar manic depressive possessed of an enormous ego. Founding Father Ben Franklin may be the nearest predicate, a billionaire by modern terms from his highly successful printing franchise operations and rumored to be quite the womanizer. We highlight these examples because all three have been romanticized and firmly cemented as saints in the American Pantheon of our historical leaders. There is no telling what personality types might serve well as President.

Unfortunately for us in the prognostication business, there is nothing inherently telling about Trump's personality or background that give clues to legislative preferences or whether he would have any commitment to a healthcare agenda as his predecessor did. We take him for what he has said, which has been (1) not much, (2) ever shifting, and (3) lacking true substance.

> There is nothing inherently telling about Trump's personality or background that give clues to legislative preferences or whether he would have any commitment to a healthcare agenda as his predecessor did.

The Trump Presidency

In the weeks since the election, Trump has continued to promise that ACA will be repealed, but has also tried to reassure the American people that his plan will maintain some of the more popular elements, such coverage for individuals with pre-existing conditions and the ability for adult children to stay on their parents' policies until age 26 even though it would add cost to the program.[9] His new administration's healthcare website still lacks specificity, even as it places even more legislative and administrative responsibilities on individual states, particularly with regard to Medicaid. Campaign rhetoric may be catching up with governing reality.

On the one hand, Trump has called for a special session of Congress specifically to repeal ObamaCare, and his team remains committed to that piece of dramatic political theater.[10] On the other hand, there has been chatter about "repeal and delay" to help manage the reality that 2017 enrollment is set and the industry will need a lot of time to adjust to whatever comes next. Many people are anticipating a "go slow" strategy to avoid an unpopular disruption of the current system until the Republicans have a workable replacement.

Medicaid Rollback? Or Expansion to a Weaker Form of Universal Coverage?

The appointment of Tom Price as Secretary of HHS suggested to many that Trump had fallen into line with the negative Republican perspective on Medicaid. His transition website contains language about pushing Medicaid off to the States in a block grant model – relying on pre-ACA enrollment figures – that would reduce the federal contribution and remove rules dictating how much and whom to cover.

The prospect of a Medicaid rollback (like the question of ensuring coverage on the exchanges) is one place where the "rubber meets the road" and Trump will need to decide where he stands. On one side, the rollback aligns with the philosophy of Secretary Price and Speaker Ryan outlined in Chapter 4. By resetting Medicaid eligibility (and block grants) back to where it was before President Obama expanded the program, the Republican plan translates into taking away federal funding from roughly 20 million Americans who gained Medicaid under the ACA and in its lead-up, as well as 12-13 million Americans who obtained insurance via subsidies on the exchanges.

Such an action risks spurring public outrage from those affected, potentially alienating affected voters. It was easy to rally people by complaining about the ACA costing jobs, taking away people's doctors, forcing them to pay more for healthcare, or causing an epidemic of people dying in the street.[11] It's going to be much harder, and probably downright impossible, to persuade the more than 30 million newly insured people or their family members and loved ones that they should give up access to care.

> *It's going to be much harder, and probably downright impossible, to persuade the more than 30 million newly insured people or their family members and loved ones that they should give up access to care.*

The people who cheered at rallies are more likely to be jeering when their coverage is threatened with being stripped away.

This tension is likely to put pressure on Trump to choose between loyalty to the fiscal discipline of the Republican vision and the political expediency of not sacrificing his popularity for ideological consistency. In some ways, this is a reflection of the same tension that has emerged between Trump's promise of a massive national infrastructure project and Republican opposition to any such major new spending. It is also a situation where Trump may have an easier time standing up to prevent something (coverage) that people already have from being taken away from them, as opposed to allocating new funds for a new initiative.

What makes this even more interesting in the healthcare context are Trump's comments during the presidential campaign, as well as at earlier points in his life, that indicate an enduring sympathy to universal coverage and, potentially even to a single-payer model. On the television program "60 Minutes," for example, Trump explicitly endorsed universal coverage: "Everybody's got to be covered. This is an un-Republican thing for me to say because a lot of times they say, 'no, no, the lower 25 percent that can't afford private.' But... I am going to take care of everybody. I don't care if it costs me votes or not. Everybody's going to be taken care of much better than they're taken care of now."

Trump's comments on this and other occasions have advocated a government-funded model, supported by anticipated savings on market reforms (such as insurance competition across state lines). His endorsement of universal coverage represents a major departure from Republican orthodoxy on an issue that is likely to come to a head if Speaker Ryan leads the Republican way on healthcare. If Trump's populist stripes are going to show, this is a key place where it is not difficult to imagine him breaking from ideological conservatives. At the same time, the coverage he protects may end up being much weaker and less effective.

Abortion
While Trump's thinking on universal coverage offers some encouragement to his political opponents, his extremist comments on abortion have scared many people. Trump's offhand suggestion on MSNBC that women who seek abortions might be subject to jail or other punishment set off a firestorm on both sides of the issue.[12] He was forced to clarify his commitment to a state's rights, pro-life stance. Several walk-backs and position changes later, his new administration's healthcare website includes an explicit commitment to protecting the innocent from the time of conception. Incoming HHS Secretary Price has been

vocal about his desire to withdraw federal funds from Planned Parenthood.

In contrast to Trump's potential wild card view of healthcare coverage, there is little reason to anticipate independence on abortion or other issues of women's health. Most observers expect President Trump to appoint a reliably conservative, pro-life Supreme Court justice to replace Justice Scalia, breaking the current 4-4 deadlock on the Court with another reliable vote on the Republican social agenda. This opens up, among other things, the possibility of the replacement of Roe v. Wade with further limitation on access to abortion.

> "Most observers expect President Trump to appoint a reliably conservative, pro-life Supreme Court justice to replace Justice Scalia,"

Big Pharma

"Because the drug companies have an unbelievable lobby. And these guys that run for office, that are on my left and right and plenty of others, they're all taken care of by the drug companies. And they're never going to put out competitive bidding. So I said to myself wow, let me do some numbers. If we competitively bid, drugs in the United States, we can save as much as $300 billion a year."

In January 2016, Trump made a statement that Medicare should negotiate directly with the drug companies and save $300 billion a year. This is directly contrary to current Republican policy. His designated HHS Secretary, Tom Price, is opposed to re-negotiating Medicare Part D.

Will this be an area of disagreement where Price is likely to lose? Given Trump's pride in his negotiating abilities and record of expressed frustration over federal overspending, there is good reason to think that President Trump will impose his personal view on this issue.

In his interview with Time magazine on November 28, he reiterated that he would bring down drug prices, singling out the pharmaceutical industry for scrutiny and potential regulation.[13] Industry leaders are worried about Trump's tendency to single companies out for criticism on Twitter, although to-date his targets have been defense contractors.

One interesting potential flashpoint will be the 21st Century Cures Act, which passed the House and Senate in late 2016. The Cures Act has managed to bring together bipartisan support from Democrats and Republicans and from patients and Big Pharma to support its allocation of $4.8 billion for health research over the next decade. Its highlights include $1.8 billion for the Cancer Moonshot Initiative championed by Vice-President Joe Biden in memory of his son, Beau, whose diagnosis of brain cancer led to an untimely passing at age 46. In addition, the Cures Act allocates $1.5 billion for President Obama's Precision Medicine Initiative, which focuses on identifying treatment and prevention strategies specifically tailored to people's unique characteristics, including their genome sequence, microbiome composition, health history, lifestyle, and diet. Another $1.5 billion of the funding is focused on the BRAIN initiative to advance understanding of the brain to help find a cure for Alzheimer's.

With its box of "goodies," the 21st Century Cures Act was embraced by the medical research community, the biotech and digital health industry, and addiction treatment providers. At the same time, it drew the ire of both progressives and conservatives for its array of handouts. It is easy to imagine President Trump joining the critics who view the bill as an excessive hand-out to the drug industry. The legislation is supposed to be funded through sales of the Strategic Petroleum Reserve, but that designation will be part of any budget the Trump Administration submits to Congress.

The Opioid Epidemic and Addiction Treatment
Undoing the Medicaid expansion that included treatment for substance abuse might undo a lot of the gains made in battling the epidemic of opioid addiction, although a state by state analysis found that the level of coverage for substance abuse does not seem to correlate with Medicaid expansion.[14] While the bulk of the 21st Century Cures Act funding is focused on biotech research, the addiction treatment community is slated to see additional $1 billion over two years on anti-opioid efforts. This funding may balance out other funding rollbacks.

Among other promising developments, the Cures Act creates a new position of Assistant Secretary for Mental Health and Substance Abuse, to be appointed by the President, which will raise the profile and consciousness about addiction treatment and mental health issues. It allocates money to combat and treat the narcotic opioid epidemic, and directs federal agencies to increase enforcement of the Mental Health Parity and Addiction Equity Act of 2008. Given the worry on the part of behavioral health community that the incoming Trump administration and Republican Congress might be in a cost-cutting mode with respect to U.S. healthcare, the public support for behavioral health treatment resources has offered reason to be hopeful.

The public support for behavioral health treatment resources has offered reason to be hopeful.

The opioid epidemic appears to be an issue that President Trump cares about. In October 2016, he gave a major policy speech in New Hampshire about his plans for confronting the continuing problem of substance abuse, which harkened back to the War on Drugs. He praised his running mate Vice-President Pence's programs in Indiana of increasing mandatory minimum sentences for drug dealers while expanding treatment programs. Trump placed a lot of emphasis on stopping the flow of illegal drugs into the country via his border wall and monitoring the postal system so that drugs could not be mailed from China, not taking into account that most of the drugs that are abused are domestically available prescription drugs and alcohol. Candidate Trump promised to tackle the opioid abuse problem on several fronts:

- Speed up FDA approval of new treatments
- Make recovery medications easier to get
- Remove the cap on number of patients a doctor can treat
- Have the DEA reclassify amount of schedule II drugs that can be manufactured/sold
- Institute the use of drug courts and mandated treatment
- Provide greater availability of Narcan for law enforcement and emergency medical workers
- Remove barriers to treatment because of Medicaid bureaucracy

Trump praised the passage of the Comprehensive Addiction

and Recovery Act as an "important step" in confronting the opioid addiction epidemic. CARA authorizes over $180 million a year for prevention, treatment, recovery, law enforcement, criminal justice reform, and overdose reversal, but the money will come from the yearly appropriations process, and so it will be subject to Congressional budgetary debates and Trump administration negotiations.

Marijuana

"[Marijuana legalization] is not something I'd be willing to do right now. . . . it's not something that I would want to do."[15] - "[D]ecide state by state In terms of marijuana and legalization, I think that should be a state issue, state-by-state. I think medical should [be dercriminalized]. And then I really believe we should leave it up to the states. And of course you have Colorado. There's a question as to how it's all working out there, you know? That's not going exactly trouble-free."[16]

Trump's approach to marijuana is a question mark. He is famous as a teetotaler, citing the premature death of his alcoholic brother, Freddy, for his abstinence. During the election, Trump did not make any firm comments about the ongoing debate over whether to legalize marijuana. His comments hedged, expressing support for decriminalization (though he did not use that specific word) of medical marijuana. As to broader decriminalization, he expressed misgivings about Colorado, which has gone further faster than other states in decriminalizing adult recreational use. His basic position, that it should be left up to individual states, is consistent with current policy.

Trump's nominee for Attorney General, Jeff Sessions, is a social conservative who is not viewed as friendly to the legalization trend. As a younger man, Sessions was an instrumental part of Nancy Reagan's "Just Say No" campaign. As Attorney General, Sessions will oversee the DEA and will have the ability to ramp up DEA enforcement. Attorney General Sessions, for example, may look for openings to challenge the federal "hands-off" policy towards marijuana in the states that have decriminalized medicinal and recreational use.

This would represent an about-face on federal policy in recent years. Many people expected the Obama administration to direct the DEA to reschedule marijuana from Schedule I of the Controlled Substances Act (meaning illegal and no recognition of medicinal use) to Schedule II (legal but subject to controls due to the high risk of abuse).

Trump's comments are not indicative of enthusiasm for this move. Reform of banking and other laws that treat marijuana the same as other illegal drugs also appears to be on the backburner.

Where Will Trump Assert Himself on Healthcare?

How active is Donald Trump likely to be on healthcare? Our suspicion is that he will start out with a more hands-on approach during and after the political show of repealing the ACA, but not sustain interest in the nitty-gritty of figuring out what to replace it with, and he will delegate the job.[17] Instead, following the ACA repeal, we expect a presidency marked by reactive, occasional surprises on healthcare issues that draw his attention and passion.

> Following the ACA repeal, we expect a presidency marked by reactive, occasional surprises on healthcare issues that draw his attention and passion.

As a result, Trump's selections for cabinet posts are likely to drive the answers to the day-to-day questions of healthcare policy ahead. Specifically, his selection of Tom Price for Secretary of Health and Human Services is likely to mean that, without Trump's own intervention, his administration will be closely in line with Ryan's "Better Way" proposal outlined in Chapter 4. This selection is likely to limit Trump's own impact other parts of healthcare policy.

On the broader range of issues, Trump may join the debate to strong-arm insurance companies or the pharmaceutical industry, but there isn't enough of a difference between his priorities (less regulation, more competition, more control on the state level) and those of the Republicans who have been thinking about this and dreaming of this opportunity for the past eight years for him to wade into the fray in a substantive way. He also is lacking a leader to take up the battle for pushing the drug companies on pricing, let alone to take on the army of drug company lobbyists who have adeptly navigated Capitol Hill for so long.

The two issues that have the most potential for divergence are the Medicaid and insurance subsidy rollback and drug pricing. At the same time that Trump's interest and ability to push successfully for an affirmative legislative agenda that departs from the Republican line is open to question, we suspect that Trump will pick his battles. In particular, we believe he will be more effective at stepping in and slowing down movement towards any reform that he regards as politically damaging, particularly stripping people of healthcare coverage. While he may not be assembling the team to build buy-in for his distinctive vision, President Trump may have a different kind of power that he is able to harness through the power of his Twitter account and the bully pulpit of the White House. If Trump's loyalists respond to his calls to action and demonstrate through their political action that they are with him on particular issues, this support may offer Trump the ability to pick his spots to rein in Republicans and drive the healthcare agenda when it matters to him.

SIX:
ENVISIONING TRUMPCARE

The Trump Promises:

Eliminate the individual mandate so Americans are not forced to buy insurance

Allow the sale of health insurance across state lines to increase competition and drive down prices

Make individual health insurance premiums tax deductible

Allow individuals to use health savings accounts (HSAs) with tax-free contributions

Require price transparency from healthcare providers, so Americans can shop prices for procedures

Provide federal grants for Medicaid, with the state determining how to allocate funding

Allow consumers access to purchase drugs and medications from overseas to increase competition and provide more options

In the last two chapters, we explored the Republican "Better Way" plan, the questions of how much daylight there may be between Speaker Ryan's vision and Donald

Trump's own articulated healthcare positions, and the likely political issues to be fought in Congress on the way to undoing ObamaCare and replacing it. In this chapter, we offer some concrete predictions about the form that TrumpCare is likely to take in coming years.

In the lead-up to this book, more than a few people questioned whether it was too risky to make predictions given the surprises that the last few months alone have brought and the unfolding drama that is still playing out between and among President Trump, Department of Health and Human Services (HHS) Secretary Price, Speaker Ryan, and Majority Leader McConnell, let alone with congressional Democrats. Acknowledging that the business of making predictions is precarious, we do so in order to look beyond the legislative changes to the impact on the ground. To the extent we get it wrong (as you read in the introduction, we've already done that), we will acknowledge those errors and recalibrate in our next edition.

As noted in Chapter 5, given our belief that President Trump is unlikely to be personally committed to a healthcare agenda beyond the media event-driven roll-back of ObamaCare and potentially pushing the drug companies on pricing, we foresee the policy agenda pivoting in favor of the direction favored by House Speaker Paul Ryan. As set out in Chapter 4, guessing where the Speaker will guide the agenda is not a mystery.

Repeal of the ACA

The showstopper piece of political theater being planned for media consumption in January 2017 is going to be the substantial repeal of the Affordable Care Act. Yes, President Trump has commented favorably on select parts of the ACA. Yes, elements of the ACA, such as the guaranteed issuance of insurance coverage irrespective of preexisting health conditions and the right of parents to keep children up to age 26 on their family policies, are very popular with the public and part of the Republican "Better Way" plan.

> The showstopper piece of political theater being planned for media consumption in January 2017 is going to be the substantial repeal of the Affordable Care Act.

Nonetheless, the repeal of the ACA simply has too much symbolic value to Republicans for them to settle for anything less. After all, as we discussed in Chapter 3, in the six years since its 2010 enactment, the Republicans made over 60 attempts to repeal the ACA. Republicans openly acknowledge the need to revive popular provisions, but only after they celebrate the death of the insurance exchanges (which were unsuccessful at creating affordable options for the high-risk pool), as well as the end of the individual and employer mandate.

Some have questioned whether Senate Democrats may be able to filibuster against repeal. We fully expect a valiant effort to prevent the straight repeal. The narrow Republican majority leaves open the possibility of a filibuster, but even if Majority Leader O'Connell does not move to block a Democratic filibuster, the budget reconciliation process and defunding offer Republicans a path to repeal that is unstoppable (assuming Republican unity). Republicans actually took this approach in December 2015, the one time when Senate Republicans joined House Republicans in the repeal vote, forcing President Obama to veto the repeal in January 2016.

This time, there will be no veto. The only questions will be how long it will take for the repeal to take effect and how long it will take President Trump and congressional Republicans to enact their own healthcare reform bill. The indications are that the repeal will be passed but delayed from taking effect on aspects of the repeal that will affect patients' coverage to allow time for a replacement. The bill vetoed by President Obama had a two-year wind down period for ACA-mandated policies, and we would expect a similar transition period.

> The only questions will be how long it will take for the repeal to take effect and how long it will take President Trump and congressional Republicans to enact their own healthcare reform bill.

The only remaining issue in replacing ObamaCare will be whether TrumpCare will be a separate tax reform package addressing just the healthcare markets, or, alternatively, delivered as a piece of a broader tax reform package addressing the entire tax code. We expect the congressional debate in 2017 to address the lost access to care and whether to offer supplemental coverage to deal with it.

TrumpCare Will Take the Form of a Tax Reform Package to Replace ObamaCare

On balance, TrumpCare, the "great healthcare plan" that will replace ObamaCare, will be a tax reform plan. The means-tested premium tax credits of ObamaCare will be replaced by a series of deductions and credits that will likely include:

- Allowing more retention of income by increasing pre-tax dollar deduction for HSAs in increased annual levels and more liberal carryover rules.

- Establishment of full deductibility for premium dollars either expended in employer-sponsored plans or in private market purchases. As with most deductions, there will be retained caps on deductibility within defined AGI limits, and minimum expense requirements for deductibility.

- For low income individuals, tax credits will be instituted to allow participation in the anticipated expanded private market offerings. The tax credits may be adjusted for age and illness ratings. It is not clear that the government will be interested in establishing a large infrastructure to make the credit adjustments, so there may be congressional engineering in establishing a sliding scale tax credit based on age only.

On balance, TrumpCare, the "great healthcare plan" that will replace ObamaCare, will be a tax reform plan.

The third element, tax credits for the poor, has the most uncertainty in predicting how in-depth the tax credit program will be. At its full extent, the credit might follow the Better Way plan and be available for intermediate payments to actually put cash in the taxpayer's pocket during the year to be able to purchase insurance in the private market during the year, rather than a credit applied to a year-end tax filing. Discussions by congressional Republicans and the Trump transition team have reportedly focused on whether there would be the apparatus to ensure that only deserving individuals would be issued the tax credit cash.

The amounts of the tax credits are also tough to anticipate.

The Ryan plan seems to limit the credit amounts to what they see were the minimum amounts needed to purchase minimal, catastrophic coverage insurance policies prior to the ACA. With the advent of the ACA and the minimum benefits requirements, these policies largely disappeared.

So there is nothing in TrumpCare that will guarantee health insurance for any individual. TrumpCare relies entirely on market participation by the insurers. What will the insurers do? What we anticipate will be a proliferation of bare-bones policies whose cost will be determined by the amount of the tax credit. Realistically, these policies won't cover much at all. To be low cost enough to be affordable by the limited tax credit, they will need to be very low benefit. These low-cost/low benefit (LC/LB) policies will have very high deductibles, copays, and coinsurance, and will provide not minimum benefits, but rather very limited benefits. Current premium costs in the market indicate that benefits will likely be one-third of those under minimum benefit bronze plans under the ACA.

It remains to be seen how efficiently insurance markets will make the LC/LB policies available. No doubt entrepreneurs will emerge, but legitimate insurance companies will be scarce, especially given the ongoing disaster of the smaller companies who came into the exchange markets on the promise of risk corridor subsidies that never materialized in sufficient amounts.

Larger companies will not want to cannibalize their full benefit plans and offer lower cost alternatives, at least not at first. The insurance market will also be hindered by practical underwriting considerations. The risk rating of lower-income, tax credit eligible people is unclear. Certainly younger people who simply paid the ACA penalty and who are relatively healthy may well apply for the credit payments to acquire LC/LB policies. They also may skip the entire event. Tax forms are often seen as "too much adulting" in the under-35 crowd, so it is entirely likely they will forego both the tax credits and buying any health insurance, even LC/LB plans. What the market will offer by way of LC/LB plans is not predictable, but we believe that, over the time of the ObamaCare wind down, new LC/LB products will emerge in most markets.

The implications for the American public are not financially positive. Means testing and verification procedures are very likely going to limit the number of Americans eligible for the tax credit. So many more people will be left out in the cold and we anticipate the number of insured people in the US to decrease. People who access the healthcare system with LC/LB plans will find (1) very little access or acceptance of such plans by most physicians, and (2) a very high level of patient responsibility for paying for healthcare they received.

People with pre-existing conditions will not necessarily seek LC/LB plans, so they will be leveraged into purchasing plans with more generous benefits, and left to offset costs for such plans with a combination of credits, deductions, and health savings accounts.

There are no guarantees of insurance, and there are no requirements that any individual needs to buy insurance. We also anticipate that the rule allowing children stay on parents' policy to age 26 and the prohibition on consideration of pre-existing conditions for underwriting will be retained in the regulations.

ACA Expansion of HSAs

The Trump Administration and Republican Congress are likely to point to the answer to increased personal financial responsibility for healthcare as being Health Savings Accounts (HSAs) that incentivize employees to control healthcare costs by allowing them to keep funds that go unspent. HSAs are a first step towards shifting the expense off of the backs of the government and insurers and into the hands of consumers, thereby increasing even more the personal financial responsibility for healthcare.

> *The Trump Administration and Republican Congress are likely to point to the answer to increased personal financial responsibility for healthcare as being Health Savings Accounts (HSAs) that incentivize employees to control healthcare costs by allowing them to keep funds that go unspent.*

Currently, employees get tax deductions (currently $3,350 individual/$6,750 family) and tax free distribution for qualified expenses, such as out-of-pocket deductibles, copayments, and prescription drugs. Look for the terms to be sweetened to incentivize more use of HSAs as a healthcare savings tool.

As noted above, TrumpCare will be a tax reform package that is predicated on the emergence of LC/LB plans, that, if not purchased through tax credit advances by low-income individuals, can be purchased from pre-tax HSA set-asides by middle-income people. (Middle and higher income individuals will have tax deductions to offset the costs of either employer-sponsored insurance or full-benefit private market insurance plans.)

Global Medicare Capitation . . .

When the Republicans work out their replacement plan, the signature initiative expected may well be to be a shift to global capitation, a payment model in which providers are paid a set amount per patient for coverage, regardless of whether that patient seeks care, for all Medicare beneficiaries, coupled with a raise in the eligibility age to 67. The net effect will be a dramatic limit to federal spending on healthcare, shifting the financial burden to individual older Americans to insure themselves and pay more out of pocket for their healthcare needs.

. . . or at Least Risk Shifting Via Value-Based Care

There is a good chance, however, that the unpopularity of tinkering with Medicare will give President Trump second thoughts. If global capitation is not enacted, President Trump is likely to continue and even accelerate the Medicare risk shifting to providers through the transition to value-based care across the hospital and post-acute care world. The interesting question will be which particular initiatives the Trump administration will embrace. We originally expected that Trump might favor risk-shifting initiatives such as the Bundled Payment for Care Initiative (BPCI) and the Comprehensive Care for Joint Replacement (CJR) program. The early indications, however, are that the incoming HHS Secretary and many Republicans are hostile to the initiatives as an overstep of federal authority.

The Republican objections seem to differentiate between shifting risk and responsibility to insurers (as a good thing) and shifting risk and responsibility to healthcare providers (a bad thing). Given that the intention of bundled payment initiatives – cost reduction and incentivizing private sector healthcare providers to make efficient choices – the Republican hostility may be attributable mostly to the role of

CMMI in the origination of these models or, alternatively, to the lobbying efforts of groups like the American Medical Association (AMA), which dislikes the model for the power it puts in the hands of hospitals.

In any case, we expect Republicans to rename and reshape their own alternative payment models (APMs), in lieu of the current models, which are currently in a trial mode. Notwithstanding the complaints about these original bundled payment models, we expect to see Republican variations in the coming two years.

Support for HMO Mergers

In order to support the money-saving expansion of global capitation, TrumpCare will attempt to give health insurers two items on their wish list: (1) a federal mandate to offer national underwriting to supplant state-by-state regulation, and (2) support for larger national entities. We believe that the former will be shot down in Congress as overreaching into states' traditional regulatory power (with perhaps some limited exceptions to offer national plans to national accounts), but that the latter will likely be the result of a more laissez faire antitrust enforcement tact, including leniency on the pending merger challenges involving Anthem and Aetna.

Scale Back of Medicaid Expansion

While it may be delayed for two years, we expect President Trump to propose to cap federal contributions to the states to fund Medicaid coverage for low-income Americans, shifting to a "block grant" model. A Republican Congress is likely to support this move. This will put pressure on states to determine whether to preserve expanded eligibility and benefits. Look for Medicaid cutbacks to result in substantial losses of coverage for able-bodied adults in many states that had expanded coverage.

Look for Medicaid cutbacks to result in substantial losses of coverage for able-bodied adults in many states that had expanded coverage.

Tougher DEA Enforcement Against Physicians and Pharmacies for Opioid Abuse (and Maybe Marijuana).

With the DEA "handcuffed" from enforcing federal laws on marijuana with increasing state decriminalization and the opioid crisis at epidemic levels nationwide, the new Trump Administration is likely to ratchet up the fight against prescription opioid abuse in all settings: interdiction against the rising problem of criminal importation and manufacture of narcotic opioids, more prosecutions of physicians and pharmacies for loose prescribing and dispensation practices (and non-use of monitoring resources), and more public health efforts to identify, prevent and treat addiction.

Under Attorney General Sessions, this effort may well be expanded to attack recreational marijuana and loose state medical marijuana systems. Look for tension between the hardline Attorney General Sessions and Congress over whether to keep the current "hands off" approach with continued delegation to states of the right to regulate marijuana as more pressing federal issues take up the national agenda.

Showdown on Pharma Pricing?

While drug overpricing has been a Democratic issue, the Republican Congress will become more hands off, allowing markets to set prices in the Pharma space. As we describe in Chapter 5, the one exception we will not be surprised to see is the "Negotiator-in-Chief" seeking to enable Medicare to negotiate prices for high-cost, low-competition drugs. President Trump's art-of-the-deal bent is likely to put pressure on drug pricing directly by intervening in certain price negotiations, and indirectly by increasing competition, including reducing the FDA biologic exclusivity period (from its current 12 years), directing the FDA to give prioritized, expedited review to biosimilar applications with limited competition in the marketplace, and accelerating the approval process for generics and other drugs drug applications.

Continued Stalemate in D.C.

Washington will stalemate as the key players assert themselves in different ways. We see the independent President Trump as largely indifferent or passive on most issues impacting healthcare once the showstopper of the ACA repeal is over, and, as a consequence, the traditional bickering of what to do next will likely pit the House against the Senate on many fronts. This is likely to translate to revision of initiatives and uncertain enactment.

As a result, while we have clarity on some pieces of the executive agenda, we predict continued stalemate in D.C. over most matters in healthcare not covered by the initial roar to repeal the ACA. As we also discussed earlier, any innovations are likely tied completely to tax reform, which no doubt will be Speaker Ryan's number one priority.

SEVEN:
THIS IS REAL: IMPLICATIONS FOR PATIENTS

What will the practical implications of TrumpCare be for patients? The answer depends on which patients we are talking about. Unsurprisingly, Americans are deeply divided on their feelings about healthcare and whether to stay the course with ObamaCare, or change directions. The 2016 election demonstrated this profound division clearly. According to a Kaiser Health Tracking Poll, 68% of all voters – of all political affiliations – described healthcare as a major issue in their voting decision.

What the transition from ObamaCare to TrumpCare will mean varies greatly based on their insurance status, their own health needs and those of loved ones, as well as which candidate or party they support. In addition, the implications vary based on where patients live. As we discuss in Chapter 3, for many patients, the decision of their home states either to expand Medicaid or hold out against expansion make a tremendous difference. These factors make the change from ObamaCare to TrumpCare a non-event for some, while potentially cataclysmic for others.

Repeal of Obamacare is almost certainly coming. For Trump voters, this was the rallying cry with which they won the day. President Trump has signaled his intention to make repealing and replacing ObamaCare with "something terrific" one of his first priorities. As we address in Chapter 6, we expect the Trump administration to make good on the promise of repeal in the first hundred days. This is despite the fact that millions of Trump supporters will lose their current healthcare as a consequence, unless the government comes up with a replacement.

For Clinton voters, the impending Trump dismantling of the ACA is cause for fear and anger. There is uncertainty about what comes next, which has many people confused and worried. Yet, despite the widespread anxiety, how they will be affected varies considerably.

Where you live is a significant factor in how you'll be affected, as some states are focused on undoing ObamaCare, while other states are preparing to move forward with their own reforms. In California, there is talk of moving to a single, self-insured state fund – a variant of single payer – overseen by a government agency, which will fill any coverage void created by repeal. Other states, like Colorado, have recently weighed or are currently weighing their own healthcare reforms. Many states with Democratic attorneys general have already announced that they are considering or actively pursuing legal challenges to any plans that will strip people of access to healthcare.

Where you live is a significant factor in how you'll be affected, as some states are focused on undoing ObamaCare, while other states are preparing to move forward with their own reforms.

Based on these differences, we examine how we expect the roll-out of TrumpCare to affect different groups of patients.

For people who are worried, understanding the anticipated legal and potentially political opposition may offer a source of comfort as campaign promises (or threats) encounter reality.

Who Benefited from ObamaCare?

For many patients, the reactions to the November 2016 election are rooted in anxiety about their own healthcare futures. Americans who did not previously have health coverage and gained it under the ACA are faced with the prospect of losing it. According to news reports, an estimated 5 to 6 million Trump supporters are actually among those ranks. On the day after the election, there was a sharp spike in ObamaCare enrollment. Over 100,000 individuals signed up for ACA coverage.

While some did not find the ObamaCare coverage helpful, for anyone in the midst of dealing with their own health problems or those of a loved one, the implications are profound. Will they lose access to medications that sustain them? For people with a chronic condition, the prospects are potentially dire - being cut off from the medications they need, the doctors they see, and the tests to tell how they are doing. The threat of loss of coverage is terrifying.

On the other hand, people who are healthy or still couldn't afford care or get what they needed under the ACA, the change is less hazardous. For some, it might even be a good thing, as long as they don't get sick. While some of those Trump voters understood they were taking a risk with their healthcare coverage but felt it was necessary based on the direction of the country or the economy, many linked their votes to dissatisfaction with ObamaCare's high deductibles and costs. In a nutshell, they felt the exchange plans were unhelpful or irrelevant and, therefore, losing them is a non-issue.

Since the ACA became law in 2010, people have been asking us about whether it was good for patients. The best answer is: it depends.

For those who had good employer coverage before the ACA and were relatively healthy and only counting on coverage for the occasional problem, then odds are that the ACA changes weren't a cause for celebration, nor will TrumpCare be a major cause for stress. After all, as a result of the ACA insurance underwriting and scope changes (such as the expansion to minimum essential benefits), you were essentially sharing a bigger pool of costs for other people's care, and paying higher premium, deductible, copayment, and coinsurance costs, without any corresponding benefit. For those who were already happy with their employer-based insurance coverage (and for people who employ others and are paying for their employees' coverage), nostalgia for the time before the ACA is not uncommon.

Of course, if you were a co-worker in the same health insurance plan as our previous example, but had a medical issue that wasn't covered by insurance, then the ACA was a vast improvement. Many parents we know who have kids on the autism spectrum, for example, discovered that "minimum essential benefits" took on real meaning when insurance companies finally started paying for the costs of developmental support, applied behavioral analysis, and therapy for their children. Before ObamaCare, insurance companies frequently denied this kind of care on the grounds that these were "educational therapy," not healthcare. The ACA removed that hurdle, opening up access to care.

Similarly, for people struggling with substance abuse, the ACA opened up the doors to insurance reimbursement for addiction treatment. Although the 2008 Mental Health Parity law had technically already mandated that insurance companies stop discriminating against mental health and addiction treatment (relative to medical care), the truth was nothing really changed in insurance denials of coverage until the ACA minimum essential benefits forced insurers to pay for care.

ObamaCare was also life-changing for those who were unemployed or lacked insurance prior to ObamaCare and had significant health challenges. A person who needed a liver transplant but was unemployed and couldn't get insurance because of a preexisting condition suddenly had access to coverage on the exchange, leading to the ability to get life-saving treatment without the prospect of financial ruin.

Unfortunately, there are also stories to be found of people who either couldn't use the insurance because they lacked the financial wherewithal to pay the deductible or were financially ruined nonetheless by their share of cost on an astronomically expensive procedure. (Even if insurance covers 80% of a $300,000 bill for an expensive treatment, the 20% coinsurance of $60,000 exceeds the median U.S. household income.) The truth is that, for some people, ACA coverage was salvation; for others, it just shifted the problem from lack of coverage to a new problem – the high cost of care.

The most profound change – and the patients who benefited the most from the ACA – were the people for whom the law opened the doors to the healthcare system that were previously closed, in many cases through the ACA's expansion of Medicaid. For many living in poverty dealing with health issues who suddenly found themselves eligible for Medicaid, the ACA was salvation.

As we address in Chapter 3, poor people living in the 19 hold-out states (as of September 2016) were not helped by the ACA, even though that was the law's intent. Consequently, odds are high that patients living at or just above poverty level in Medicaid hold-out states have not been helped by the ACA. Without Medicaid, the available subsidized exchange policies often came with deductibles and coinsurance that made these policies financially out of reach. Those with incomes too high for Medicaid, but too low to qualify for federal subsidies on the Obamacare exchanges, fell into a unintended coverage gap, though it would be unfair to blame ObamaCare for that particular failure.

Who Will Benefit from TrumpCare?

Like the ACA, TrumpCare has very different implications for different patients. For reasonably healthy people and for people for whom insurance has not been a helpful structure – based either on the unaffordability of their individual share of the cost, or the lack of health expenses to justify the expense of the monthly premiums – the change to TrumpCare may be a positive thing. At the very least, it saves them money that they were spending without any obvious return.

For younger, healthier people, the end of the individual mandate will eliminate the pressure to buy insurance and the threat of a tax penalty. Statistically, major health problems are unlikely until a person's late 50s/early 60s. During their younger, healthier years, sudden emergencies can be dealt with through EMTALA, which entitles them to show up at a hospital and demand care. The potential financial consequences of emergency care are serious, but good asset protection or bankruptcy offer protection.

For people who are not earning enough to take advantage of insurance benefits, TrumpCare and the shift to health savings accounts (HSAs) and high-deductible health plans (HDHPs) offers a chance to exercise consumer power in favor of better, cheaper care. In Chapter 9, we explore the growing trend of "direct care" options, where healthcare providers offer consumers the option of more affordable care that bypasses insurance and sets prices that people are willing to pay. This trend has not received significant attention in recent years, as the primary focus has been on fixing insurance-covered healthcare. We have heard from direct care providers who believe that the ACA unintentionally suppressed consumer interest in these options because it kept the middle class oriented towards insurance, where out-of-pocket costs were controlled.

As noted in Chapter 6, President Trump's solutions are likely to be focused on tax credits for healthcare premiums (age-adjusted and refundable for the uninsured), HSAs that incentivize employees to control healthcare costs by allowing them to keep funds that go unspent (coupled with high-deductible plans), and national underwriting in lieu of state-by-state insurance regulation.

All of these measures incentivize individuals to be better healthcare consumers. This is a boon for price-efficient cash-pay services, but these solutions fail to address the astronomical costs for catastrophic care and expensive chronic conditions.

Widening Disparities in Funding and Resources for the Poor and Elderly

One thing that is abundantly clear is that the repeal of ObamaCare and the implementation of TrumpCare will likely lead to even greater geographic disparities in healthcare coverage for those living at or near poverty, since states control Medicaid implementation. The gap is also likely to widen through greater flexibility for states in their Medicaid program design. Some states will continue to fund Medicaid in absence of federal funding. More progressive states (e.g., California and Colorado) are likelier to absorb the cost of retaining the ACA's expanded Medicaid coverage to the millions of the poorest residents who are losing federal funding.

> One thing that is abundantly clear is that the repeal of ObamaCare and the implementation of TrumpCare will likely lead to even greater geographic disparities in healthcare coverage for those living at or near poverty, since states control Medicaid implementation.

Others (19 hold-out states) never took the ACA money, and kept Medicaid "skinny." These states, which never accepted funding for Medicaid expansion, will continue to limit coverage to the "safety net" population, leaving their poorest residents without access to care. This is unlikely to get better for poor people, and may even worsen, under TrumpCare.

A third group of states expanded Medicaid with the infusion of the federal funds, but in absence of these funds, may not have political support to make up the difference. These states will have to decide how much to soften the blow for the millions who lose coverage via the ObamaCare repeal.

If and when defunding kicks in, the repeal of the ACA would also be likely to expand healthcare inequalities among the elderly. Within Medicare, capitation would widen the gap between the "haves" (who are already utilizing the Medicare Advantage Program and supplemental insurance to improve their access) and the "have-nots." TrumpCare spending caps are likely to limit end-of-life care and expensive care for chronic conditions, such as diabetes and chronic obstructive pulmonary disease (COPD), for beneficiaries who are unable to pay out of pocket for costs beyond their personal capitation.

Growing State Experimentation

In the face of the federal roll-back and the explicit Republican goal of shifting the responsibility for healthcare to the states, we may see more state-by-state experimentation with healthcare reform. Many states, for example, are likely to respond to federal cuts by advancing their own statewide healthcare reform programs. California has begun to consider the option of self-funding its own health plan.

Some states have had their own reforms implemented for many years, while others have considered experiments:

Hawaii: In 1974, Hawaii passed a mandate for employers to provide health insurance for any person employed more than 20 hours a week. Hawaii was also an early adopter of reform to address insurance gaps, adding coverage in 1989 for people who were not covered by either Medicaid or employer-based coverage.

Massachusetts: As noted in Chapter 2, Massachusetts

earned Governor Romney fame for a 2006 plan that incorporated an "individual" mandate that Massachusetts residents obtain at least a minimum level of health insurance coverage, an employer mandate that Massachusetts employers with at least ten full-time equivalents (FTEs) provide health insurance coverage, and free healthcare insurance for Massachusetts residents earning less than 150% of the federal poverty level (FPL).

VermontCare: Vermont enacted the nation's first single-payer healthcare system in 2011, although it was abandoned before implementation. Green Mountain Care was intended to be a state-funded and managed insurance pool that would provide near-universal coverage to residents. The decision to scrap the program in 2014 was a financial one: funding the program would require an unsustainable increase in taxes on smaller businesses in the state.

ColoradoCare. In the November 2016 election, Coloradans voted to reject ColoradoCare, an opt-in single payer, universal coverage model. Patients who preferred their existing private insurance of federal coverage could keep it, but the state public health system would shift to single payer, with costs covered by a new 10% income tax allocated on employers (6.67%) and employees (3.33%), as well as a tax on non-payroll income. In the November 2016 election, ColoradoCare was soundly defeated because of cost concerns.

The Vermont and Colorado experiences highlight that bold state-level reform faces the challenge of anxiety over potential costs. Nonetheless, in the event that efforts to strip residents of coverage become a serious reality, it is easy to imagine greater receptivity to single payer in progressive, Democratic-led states.

Legal Battles and Public Backlash May Slow the Process

Patients may get a reprieve from these and other TrumpCare changes if state attorney generals take a page out of the Republican playbook and sue the administration to challenge each action that rolls back healthcare in court. TrumpCare is likely to incorporate many of the Republican ideas that have been touted by national and state opponents of ObamaCare, but the question remains whether Democratic attorney generals and Republican extremists will continue the legal challenges.

The loss of insurance or Medicaid is going to be a problem for many people and there is a political showdown coming. Whatever the replacement version of the coverage expansion might be – likely a tax credit reform of some kind – it is clear that there will be a two-year phase out/phase in process. This two year transition window was articulated in the last attempt by Republicans to repeal ObamaCare, which the GOP-controlled House of Representatives sent to Obama for veto.

One big question is how difficult patients will make it for Republicans to roll back the expansion of coverage for the over 20 million people who obtained it via the ACA in those two years. Will patients protest? Or will this issue get lost in the shuffle? Some of it will depend on the ability of ACA supporters to organize and drive grassroots campaigns to express the importance of the ACA.

Regardless of whether you were an ACA proponent or opponent, a few things are clear: The ACA was a significant improvement in healthcare access for millions of Americans, even while it had many detractors and shortcomings. There is a lot of uncertainty and anxiety about ACA repeal, especially among those whose lives were made much better by it.

> *The ACA was a significant improvement in healthcare access for millions of Americans, even while it had many detractors and shortcomings.*

But the process of repeal and replacement of ObamaCare won't happen overnight. It will be relatively slow, with multiple opportunities for consumers to weigh in and let lawmakers at all levels know how they feel about the proposed changes. It will be even slower if patients who are losing coverage organize effectively and vigorously to voice their views, and if Democrats challenge the incoming policies with even a fraction of the zeal with which Republicans pursued the repeal of ObamaCare. Finally, healthcare reform is likely to be a central issue for lawmakers on both sides of the aisle in the 2018 midterm elections.

EIGHT:
UNPREPARED?
IMPLICATIONS FOR THE
HEALTHCARE INDUSTRY

The whipsawing impact of Trump's election victory on the healthcare industry will be enormous. "Yuuuge" in fact. With ObamaCare, once concepts were merely discussed in Washington in 2009, the healthcare industry adapted almost overnight to variations of concepts the policymakers were examining. Commercial insurers listened to government presentations on pay for performance, bundled payments, and non-traditional alternatives to fee-for-service reimbursement with varying effects, thinking about how to integrate them into the private insurance marketplace. Hospitals especially were forced to look outside of their own four walls to examine how they were going to cope with the coming regulations. "Population health" became a new buzzword, and rumors of massive penalties for "bounce-back" patients dominated conferences and cocktail parties.

Finally, the ACA was passed, and regulations followed. By 2011, most parts of the healthcare system had digested the changes and had a pretty good idea where the world was headed and what was being expected of them. As massive investments were made in computer systems of all kinds, the ACA touched off consolidation on an unprecedented scale.

Managers scrambled to put more clinical operations under one roof to spread the gigantic IT costs over more beds, more patients, more doctors, and more services. Hospitals, health systems, and insurance system made enormous investments into multi-level of care infrastructure, acquiring thousands of physician practices, and established at least contractual "network" arrangements with specific nursing homes, hospice, pharmacies, and providers of all kinds.

In short, ObamaCare led to five years of frenetic rearranging of how healthcare providers did business and how they got paid, It drove decisions about who to do business with and realigned the purpose, mission, and strategy of most major healthcare organizations. And then, upon the events of one recent November night, healthcare providers had the rug pulled out from underneath them. From a provider perspective, little to nothing of the ACA or its purposes are likely to remain relevant for long in the Trump administration.

So administrators of healthcare organizations face one huge dilemma: what the hell are you supposed to do now? Wait out the four years and figure that a Democrat will regain the White House in 2020 and re-implement the ACA? Assume the ACA is gone forever and revert to pre-2009 fee-for-service models while waiting to see what, if anything, the Trump administration does to replace the ACA? Do nothing and assume that, despite the change in presidential administrations, the timing of anything new will take the bureaucrats years to implement? In short, healthcare organizations are in a quandary about where this is all heading on a practical, day-to-day operational level.

What we see is a medley of factors both slowing and constraining a departure from the ACA and in some instances, increasing the impact of ACA principles. Remember that, as we argue in Chapter 4, what we see being offered to replace the ACA will be tax reform measures, not heavy on central clinical policy. As a consequence, clinicians, from a delivery system standpoint are probably seeing today what will continue into the next four years.

Moreover, many facets of the healthcare regulatory agenda embedded in the ACA have bipartisan support, such as expansion of managed care principles (whether by ACO, as was the case in ObamaCare, or through MA expansion, which is what we expect under TrumpCare), so some financial concepts will not experience any significant change based on the transition from President Obama to President Trump. But some will, particularly those sectors that rely on Medicaid funding, and these changes may be very rough on the industry indeed.

So let's break it down and address where we see change and where we do not.

Payments and Risk Shifting to Providers
One of the few areas likely to see bipartisan support and continue under President Trump is the Medicare risk shifting to providers. The question is which initiatives will survive the transition. From a strategic standpoint, we see less imperative for provider-driven risk management – in other words, ACOs – and more imperative for insurance company driven risk management – in other words, expansion of Medicare Advantage.

This is a subtle but important difference. Both policies reach an expanded use of managed care principles to more and more Medicare patients. In the ACO model, clinical operators control the patients. The ACO model asked them to think and act a little more like insurance companies, and to hire case managers to directly initiate care protocols for all patients assigned to the ACO on the care quality metrics deemed important by CMS. When clinical operators do this, their belief systems are still largely centered on care for the patients. Coordinating that care is still the most important value. The cost of such coordination is left for administrators to cover through unique design elements in the ACO setting. The financial savings (adoption of risk by the providers) is based upon voluntary adoption by the providers as a way to better access care for their patients.

Contrast this to the Medicare expansion model, where financial entities control the patients and assign them to providers. In so doing, MA plans were left to act a little more like clinical companies. While insurance companies will have medical directors and clinical care protocols, their overriding highest value is return to shareholders, not care for patients. As a consequence, financial considerations will dominate their decision-making. And what this financial imperative at the top means is that the insurance companies will seek all the ways they can to transfer the incidence of cost of care risk onto the backs to providers to optimize the insurance companies' financial returns.

This transfer of risk is not voluntarily accepted by providers in the same sense as it was in an ACO. Instead, participating providers agree to this as the condition imposed to getting access to the patients in the first place. In the healthcare industry, this is sometimes referred to as "controlling the front end of the food chain," i.e. the patients. It makes a big financial difference to providers. When providers control the front end of the food chain, they do better financially than they do when the insurers control the front end of the food chain. That's because they control the purchasing of ancillary business (the pharmacy benefit manager, for instance) and make additional investments that truly reduce overall patients costs -- services like centralized, pre-surgical clinics and diabetes management clinics that reduce hospital days.

We have seen super successful physician-run MA programs reduce annual hospital bed days below 700 per thousand program members, while regular managed care insurance-run programs average around 1,200 days per thousand patients and fee-for-service Medicare can run upwards of 2,000 days per thousand.) When physicians don't control the front end of the food chain, they tend to not make such investments, since the patients can be pulled out from underneath them at any time, and the insurance plans tend to use that fact as leverage.

So, on balance, we see the insurance companies prevailing in this war for control of patients as more and more patients are shifted into managed care. As we argue in Chapter 6, we think that MA expansion under TrumpCare is going to be accelerated due to the overall cost savings involved. We think that the push for global capitation, in which the insurance company fixes its payments to the providers and then leaves the providers to wrestle amongst themselves for their share of funding, is going to become the norm for Medicare over the next four to eight years. After fighting with each other for funding allocations, providers will then implement care allocation protocols to keep from going broke if the patients are sicker and in need of more service or more intense services than anticipated. To survive this scrum, providers will need to become very sophisticated in both patient management. Alternatively, they can bluntly deny care, shorten hospital stays, and reduce pharmaceuticals. They can also utilize financial protection mechanisms, like purchasing stop loss insurance.

On remaining fee-for service Medicare, we will see additional risk shifting to providers as well. The Republicans were cool to the initial bundled payment initiatives proposed by the dreaded Center for Medicare and Medicaid Innovation (CMMI), but are likely to embrace other alternative payment models due to their ability to control and reduce federal spending while driving efficiency and improved healthcare outcomes.

The Medicare Access and CHIP Reauthorization Act of 2015 (MACRA) was a major initiative in the "volume to value" transition – shifting U.S. healthcare reimbursement away from episodic, purely volume-based reimbursement towards value-based, coordinate care models, with the goal of increasing efficiency and reducing healthcare costs. It replaced the old (and broken) Sustainable Growth Rate (SGR) formula with two new payment programs: the Medicare-Based Incentive Payment System (MIPS) and the Alternative Payment Model (APM). In a nutshell, the MIPS Programs offers additional payments to healthcare professionals for delivering exceptional quality. It wraps together three previously distinct quality programs: value-based modifiers, Physician Quality Reporting System (PQRS), and electronic health record (EHR) Meaningful Use incentives.

MACRA appears to enjoy bipartisan popularity. As a consequence, its implementation is likely to continue, rewarding doctors who demonstrate superior outcomes. MACRA has an ambitious target of linking at least half of Medicare payments to quality- and value-based alternative payment models by the end of 2018.

Fraud and Abuse Enforcement Continues to Expand

Another aspect of the ACA that enjoy bipartisan support was the expansion and strengthening of anti-fraud and abuse provisions in federal law. Beyond the shared goals of prevention, detection, and enforcement effort against Medicare, Medicaid, and other federal health program fraud, Republicans and Democrats are equally enthusiastic about the government's ability to reduce spending and even make money by fighting fraud.

As a result, healthcare providers should expect the anti-fraud provisions of the ACA and the enforcement climate to remain unchanged. The ACA funded numerous new anti-fraud efforts, including imposing new screening and compliance requirements, improving data sharing to enable law enforcement to cooperate, and establishing new penalties. As a result of ACA-related changes, providers were forced to jump through many more hoops, including background checks and site visits. Providers were also subjected to various audit programs, such as the Recovery Audit Contractor (RAC) audits, through which moneys paid in error by the government may be clawed back, reducing government expense in the process.

Perhaps the most significant anti-fraud change wrought by the ACA was the so-called 60-Day Rule, which required any healthcare provider who received an overpayment from Medicare or Medicaid to report and return the money no later than 60 days after the overpayment was identified. Providers who failed to report and return money were not only subject to potential penalties, but to liability under the federal False Claims Act. This change opened the door to many more whistleblowers to bring cases to the attention of the Department of Justice. This trend will likely continue. The burdens of compliance and anti-fraud efforts are likely to continue to rise under the Trump administration, as will the risks of whistleblower cases and government investigations.

Beyond these top level impacts of more risk-shifting to providers, whether by managed care population increases or by alternative value-payments models, and continued aggressive enforcement efforts, what else can particular healthcare sectors expect from TrumpCare. Below, we offer "grades" of how each vertical can expect to fare.

Hospitals - Bottom Line TrumpCare Grade: "D-" (More pain and suffering)

If the stock market reaction to the election results were indicative, hospitals are in for a rough time under a Trump administration. The ostensible reason for the plummeting hospital stock prices was the question of whether hospitals are going to lose all of the benefits from the ACA, without shedding any of the risks they accepted in the process. We think that is exactly what is going to happen over time.

The chief benefits to hospitals under the ACA were the expansions of insured patients with robust coverage, and the reduction in no-pay ER patients through Medicaid expansion. With the likely reversal of both of these elements under TrumpCare, hospitals are poised to suffer.

Even as TrumpCare will prompt coverage through tax credits, as we discussed in Chapter 7, these credits will not allow patients to afford robust plans. They will instead turn to Low Cost/Low Benefit plans and HSA savings to meet hospital costs. This means more hospital losses; the higher level of financial responsibility the individual patient has, the lower the amounts that hospitals collect. TrumpCare will expand individual financial responsibility, and hospitals will lose relative to their performance under the ACA programs.

Even before the ACA, changes in federal laws and regulations in recent years created an increasingly challenging financial environment for hospitals. A series of Medicare changes – such as readmission penalties, reductions in reimbursement for hospital-acquired conditions (HACs), and rules requiring short stays to be treated as outpatient observations with lower reimbursement than admissions – suppressed utilization and reimbursement of hospitals. The goal was to drive patients to lower level care settings, which in turn are expected to manage higher levels of acuity. Hospitals nationwide saw their censuses fall as a result.

Under the ACA, acute care hospitals were subjected to significant cuts. The basic idea was that, with fewer uninsured patients imposing the cost of unreimbursed care and with more money from taking care insured patients, hospitals could afford to give up some of the funding sources they had depended on. (Remember that to fund the large no-pay population coming into hospitals under EMTALA, hospitals did everything they could to obtain higher than average funding from other sources to offset these losses.) The ACA, for example, was supposed to cut Medicaid Disproportionate Share Hospital (DSH) payments, which are intended to support hospitals with larger shares of Medicaid and uninsured patients to help cover the costs of uncompensated care with the intention that the cuts would be balanced by an influx of payments from newly insured patients. These cuts were delayed and had not yet taken effect, leaving open the question of whether or not the repeal in the ACA will include a cancellation of these cuts. We anticipate that the Republicans will move forward with the DSH cuts as Speaker Ryan presses hard to balance the federal budget.

Under the ACA, hospitals in Medicaid expansion states did better than hospitals in hold-out states, based on the additional Medicaid revenue and decreased uncompensated costs. Now, hospitals in these states are looking at a return to unfunded care. The Republican plan to limit Medicare spending further holds out the bleak prospect that things could deteriorate further for hospitals.

At bottom, the hospitals in Medicaid hold-out states never experienced increased offset funding, and will not see an impact on the reversion. It will be business as usual, with continuing pressure to cost-shift to make up lost revenues from serving Medicaid patients. Hospitals in expansion states. By contrast, will see a gradual revenue loss. The transition to block grant funding will take some time. States are going to face tough choices as many people coming off exchange programs as they fold will also seek additional Medicaid coverage to some extent, putting additional financial pressure on States. Cuts to coverage and hospital service reimbursements seems rather inevitable for all Medicaid programs as federal funding decreases over time.

Worse still, while pre-ACA hospitals were able to exert some leverage on commercial insurers to achieve reimbursement rates to offset the losses for no-pay and under-pay patients, we see this leverage disappearing. As discussed later in this chapter, we see insurance companies as the big winners under TrumpCare, and we think that the hospitals' ability to shift revenue onto commercial plans will be significantly limited.

There are more subtle effects of ACA repeal that will impact hospitals. We are assuming that everyone who had to merge to meet the IT demands has already done so, and that further consolidations would be pushed by the alternative payment models that rewarded or penalized hospitals for out-of-the-hospital management of the patients and interacting with physicians and other providers. Will there be continuing pressure for consolidation? We believe there will be, as a result of a "survivor mode" mentality as revenues dry up with the advent or more individual patient responsibility.

The repeal of the ACA, to the extent it reduces or eliminates the out-of-the-hospital patient management, would seem to be a potential benefit. But the hospitals will not necessarily see an uptick in fee-for-service revenue as a result. Future utilization by a person who loses their exchange-based Bronze plan and now has a LC/LB plan with greater individual financial responsibility may not seek out the healthcare in the first place. Of course, there may be no reason to repeal the pain/reward compensation models, as they do save Medicare money. Even if repealed, the managed care MA patients will require coordination and case management, resulting in continuing costs for hospitals.

Finally, the ACA programs at least provided a certain degree of predictability once the regulations were fleshed out and it was up and running. The mere uncertainty over the next year while the government and the private sector seek new directions will almost certainly halt innovation, capital investment, and mergers. Hospitals have little choice but to play a wait-and see game.

Physicians and Health Professionals – Bottom Line TrumpCare Grade: "B" (A Mixed Bag)

Physicians are a mixed bag under TrumpCare. To the extent that TrumpCare returns physician payments to the traditional pre-ACA fee-for-service world, they will once again be incentivized to perform procedures and seek and acquire the highest paying patients. We envision that the AMA will lobby successfully for a more fee-for-service world. This will work for Medicare, as we think the Trump administration will be sympathetic to physicians, as evidenced in Chapter 4 by Speaker Ryan's signaling the return of physician-owned hospitals.

But while physicians as a whole may do better with TrumpCare Medicare than under the ACA, we think this will be tempered by the behavior of the true winners under TrumpCare: the insurance companies. We foresee that the insurance companies will lobby for and receive key powers, all in the name of constraining healthcare costs. As a result, insurance companies will be able to engage in negotiations and deploy "blunt force trauma" on providers. Physicians will be forced to accept low rates to access any patients at all in what we foresee as newly approved narrow networks and interstate plan designs. In essence, we see commercial insurers dictating rates to providers, and MA insurers transferring all risk to providers under global capitation programs.

Larger, hospital-affiliated physician groups will find their hospital partners addled by the uncertainty for a while, and then less inclined to coordinate care (or to be more precise, pay for the coordination of care) with the repeal of the ACA. These kinds of large, hospital-centric organizations will increasingly rely on global capitation, which, by its very structure sets doctors off against hospitals and other providers to gain their fair share of the fixed dollar amounts paid in such programs.

We believe we will see continued migration to concierge medicine in those areas supporting wealthier populations. Primary care physicians will remain valuable to narrow network commercial plans and MA programs, and should continue to experience growth and steady revenues. We caution that there is a generational shift occurring in primary care, with older physicians still seeking out fee-for-service models, and younger doctors content with managed care, salaried models that only require them to show up certain fixed hours per week. To the extent that more and more doctors seek salaried positions, the insurance plans will be under as much pressure to address rates in the fee-for service markets.

Physician specialists would seemingly benefit greatly from the ACA repeal under TrumpCare. More than any other sector of healthcare providers, specialists live and die by the number of procedure/number of referrals they receive. While larger organizations were given incentives to weed down the number of specialists on their panels, the pressure to reduce panel sizes will likely not be as great under TrumpCare. At the same time, it will not be all blue skies for specialists. The reduction in the number of robust insurance policyholders over time, and the increase in MA population, will mean there will be fewer patients accessing specialist services (or at least with the ability to pay) and the pressure to compete for and participate in managed care and narrow network panels will continue.

Post-Acute Providers – Bottom Line TrumpCare Grade: "B+"

Post-acute providers – skilled nursing facilities (SNFs), home health agencies (HHAs), and hospices – may see a silver lining in a Trump presidency. While the legislative and regulatory changes of the last decade have forced significant changes for acute care hospitals, post-acute providers enjoyed relatively little disruption from a period of Medicare-driven profitability. That trend was beginning to change towards the end of the Obama administration. Fraud and abuse enforcement was continuing to expand. Dark clouds of a changing system were on the horizon. In September 2016, the Centers for Medicare and Medicaid (CMS) released the "Mega-Rule" for nursing homes, which included significant changes and new burdens. In over 700 pages (including commentary), the Mega-Rule spelled out numerous ways in which Medicare was looking for nursing homes to do more, without any concomitant increase in reimbursement. Changes included limitations on facility use of arbitration to resolve resident disputes, a focus on treating higher levels of acuity in the post-acute setting, reducing hospital readmissions, and requiring greater attention to behavioral health needs of facility residents.

Beyond heightened regulatory requirements starting to take effect, nursing homes and post-acute providers have been at greater risk in an ACA-driven bundled payment environment because health systems and acute care hospitals have more incentive to be selective about their utilization. After all, hospitals will retain more of the payment bundle if they avoid a patient stay in a nursing home or get patients to absorb the cost of private home care, in lieu of Medicare-reimbursed home health agency visits. This trend has already been evident under CMMI's Comprehensive Care for Joint Replacement (CJR) program which launched in April 2016. Under the CJR Program, payment is bundled for a 90-day episode of care that begins with a hip or knee replacement. The early results have shown a decided reduction in referrals to SNFs for the simple fact that, if a patient can be discharged home instead, the hospital holds onto more of the bundled payment.

Consequently, SNFs are anticipating some relief from the repeal of the ACA. In particular, Trump's designated HHS Secretary Tom Price, has criticized the CJR program as exceeding CMS authority and interfering in clinical decision-making. The big question will be how CJR and bundled payment initiatives will be impeded.

Also impacting SNFs (as well as other providers such as home health and hospice) are Department of Labor regulations and a national minimum wage increase. If the Department of Labor is more business friendly and the national minimum wage increase goes off the table for four years, the larger employers of low wage labor like SNFs will benefit.

Home health and hospice providers will find fewer hospitals courting them as preferred providers as hospitals will be under less pressure to manage the out-of-hospital care of patients. Fee-for-service emphasis should benefit them in traditional Medicare circles. On the other hand, they will have the least leverage at the table when vying for their share of global cap dollars with doctors and hospitals in MA programs. We actually do see some pressure for continued horizontal integration of these providers as smaller entities will not have the infrastructure (or capital for infrastructure) needed in healthcare going forward.

Senior Care Providers: Bottom Line TrumpCare Grade: "A"

For assisted living facilities, the past decade has been a boom time. The aging of the Baby Boomers has brought a rising tide of seniors, living longer into assisted living facilities and continuing care retirement communities (CCRCs). These facilities are largely privately funded, so they are unlikely to be affected in a significant way by the change of presidential administrations. Moreover, they are already dependent upon the tax status of their residents, so they are in some ways the "ideal" healthcare facility under Speaker Ryan's view of the world: state regulated or unregulated and providing relatively minimal care, mostly personal support in daily living rather than healthcare per se, and doing so with private dollars for which the tax code allows deductions.

Similarly, the trend on other forms of senior care, such as private home care, is likely to continue to grow – not because of any continuation or change in policy from President Obama to President Trump, but simply because these services are well positioned for growth based on social trends. People are living longer and either aging seniors or their adult children will need to pay, principally out-of-pocket – for care at home and other resources.

Federal Qualified Health Centers and Other Community Clinics - Bottom Line TrumpCare Grade: "D-"

Federally qualified health centers (FQHCs), rural health clinics (RHCs), and other federally funded community clinics are bracing for trouble under a Trump administration. While Hillary Clinton frequently brought up these safety net providers, which serve predominantly poor patients, as part of her reform plans, they were not part of Donald Trump's focus. This contrast was not surprising. Democrats tend to champion federally-funded clinics, while Republicans are notably less enthusiastic about them.

We expect FQHCs and community clinics to be a target for funding cuts in coming years. They were expected to be big winners under the ACA as a result of the increased coverage for their target population through Medicaid expansion and exchange-based subsidies. With their philosophy of treating patients without regard to ability to pay and on a sliding scale basis, FQHCs aligned with this newly covered populations.

In fact, the picture for FQHCs and other community clinics under the ACA turned out to be mixed. While some clinics grew in states that accepted Medicaid expansion funds, clinics in Medicaid Hold-out States struggled. The coming years are expected to bring less Medicaid money and less federal grant funding. We anticipate that there will be struggles and closures for these clinics without states back-filling lost federal dollars.

Behavioral Healthcare Providers – Bottom Line TrumpCare Grade: "Incomplete"

Behavioral healthcare providers face a number of unknowns from the Trump administration. Behavioral healthcare had benefited from two significant recent federal legal changes – one of which is now in the firing line. In 2009, the Mental Health Parity and Addiction Equity Act (MHPAEA) prohibited discrimination by insurers against behavioral health treatment, including addiction treatment, mental health, and youth and family developmental services (such as for children on the autism spectrum).

The ACA included those all of those services in the minimum essential benefits requirement for health plans. As we discuss in Chapter 7, the result was several years explosive growth for behavioral health.

Mental Health Parity may remain a priority under a Trump administration (even if just a softer one). As we discuss in

Chapter 5, Trump himself has expressed concern for the national opioid epidemic. The health plans still have far to go to achieve the goal of non-discrimination against behavioral health conditions, in comparison to medical treatment. The minimum essential benefits requirements, on the other hand, are chief among of the elements of the ACA in Republican sights for change. If health plans are freed from a requirement to cover addiction treatment or developmental services, will they use their freedom to retreat from behavioral coverage? Time will tell. There is reason to believe that the Trump administration will continue to require behavioral health coverage of insurance companies as one of the quid pro quo trades for the massive favors we expect to be granted to the plans.

One silver lining for addiction treatment providers in the waning days of the Obama administration was the 21st Century Cures Act, which was signed into law in December 2016 with bipartisan support. The Cures Act creates a new position of Assistant Secretary for Mental Health and Substance Abuse, to be appointed by the president, which will raise the profile and consciousness about addiction treatment and mental health issues. The Cures Act also directs federal agencies to increase enforcement of the Parity Act and allocates additional funds to combatting the narcotic opioid epidemic and treating addiction. With Trump devoting significant attention on the American opioid epidemic during the campaign and with public support for behavioral health treatment resources, the big question will be how much the Trump administration and the Republican Congress will pressure insurance companies to continue funding addiction treatment.

Pharmacies, Laboratories, and Other Ancillary Services – Bottom Line TrumpCare Grade: "C"

We lump these providers together but frankly each will suffer a slightly different fate. Laboratories will be among the least impacted groups, especially if the anticipated retention of behavioral health coverage by commercial insurers continues. While hospitals and SNFs may see some redistribution of patients between them, regardless of the patient setting, the physicians will continue to order lab tests. Labs are the archetypical countercyclical healthcare service; lab tests are a constant for healthcare regardless of who is paying and how much it costs.

Pharmacies are a different story. The Republicans are hostile to one of the few growth areas for pharmacies, the 340B program that leverages low cost drugs for the Medicaid population. There have been reported abuses, and Republicans will likely just want to shut the program down and remand the purchasing of drugs for Medicaid patients to state purchasing agencies. Beyond 340B, the marketplace has largely commoditized pharmacy services through the work of large insurance plans and prescription by mail services. We expect the trend to continue, unrelated to ACA repeal. We also expect the state-level attacks on compounding pharmacies for abuse in workers compensation programs to continue.

Other ancillary clinical services will likely see pressure to secure funding and lower prices; infusion services already took a 95% revenue hit in the Cures Act, and we expect durable medical equipment (DME) providers and dietician services to be under price pressure as well in either a fee-for-service or managed care Medicare environment.

Life Sciences (Pharma/Biotech and Medical Devices) – Bottom Line TrumpCare Grade "B"

In the aftermath of the Trump election victory, biotech stocks surged, apparently in anticipation of a laissez faire attitude towards drug prices (and resulting profits) from President Trump, in contrast to the fear of potential price controls to combat "over-pricing" of high cost-drugs under a Clinton presidency. While it is true that Hillary Clinton was the more outspoken candidate on issues like the Mylan price increases for the epi-pen, there are several reasons why the life sciences industry may come to rethink its optimism about a Trump presidency.

One aspect of industry enthusiasm is the expectation that the Trump administration will not only continue but accelerate efforts to expedite the approval process for drugs and devices. To a large extent this has been a bipartisan policy under President Obama, and the concern was focused on a change under a Clinton administration.

In 2016, for example, the industry reached agreements that establish FDA performance improvement goals through the reauthorization of a series of user fee acts, including the Prescription Drug User Fee Act (PDUFA), the Medical Device User Fee Act (MDUFA), the Generic Drug User Fee Act (GDUFA), and the Biosimilars User Fee Act (BsUFA). The Cures Act also substantially paved the way for fast-tracking of innovative treatments and took software as a medical device regulation off the table. Under the user fee system, each manufacturer category – drug manufacturers, medical device companies, generic drug makers, and biosimilars companies – pay fees to the FDA when they register their businesses and products, as well as whenever they submit applications (e.g., for new drugs or devices) to the FDA.

The FDA is supposed to utilize the user fees to improve its efficiency, with the goal of shortening the approval process cycle in bringing safe, effective products to market. The pace of FDA review and approval came up in the presidential campaign, particularly with respect to the enormous backlog in certain areas, such as increasingly costly generic drugs. There is every reason to think that the Republican Congress and President Trump will approve the user fee agreements and look for additional ways to accelerate the approval process.

At the same time, there is ample reason to think that President Trump, as a free-wheeling populist and as a business focused on negotiating good deals and undoing bad ones, may rethink the policy under which the Medicare program's hands are tied against negotiating drug prices. It is not difficult to imagine Trump looking for ways to walk away from the Medicare Prescription Drug, Improvement, and Modernization Act – the other law besides the ACA that gave the pharmaceutical lobby carte blanche in setting drug pricing and stripped the government of its power to negotiate. The industry had negotiated with the Obama administration to be largely left alone under the ACA, but it would not be a surprise to see President Trump seek to enable price negotiation for high-cost, low-competition drugs.

Beyond Trump's populist bent, the big question for the industry is where the money will come from to pay for expensive drugs and devices. For example, if the Republicans follow through on plans for global Medicare capitation, patients who cannot afford out-of-pocket expenses may be forced to forego expensive drugs and devices. For some life sciences companies, this may translate into the shrinking of already small markets for various therapeutics. For all drug and device makers, the shift to more patient financial responsibility may lead to reduced profits as they are forced to drop prices to meet the real out-of-pocket market. Given the Republican commitment to less government funding, it is worth questioning how bullish the pharmaceutical industry will be about President Trump.

Digital Health – Bottom Line TrumpCare Grade "A"

For digital health ventures looking to capitalize on increasing consumerism in patient behavior, home-based aging in place, and other lower-cost, technology-driven solutions, the net effect of requiring more out-of-pocket spending is likely to be positive. For many people, the ACA's broader coverage left less incentive to spend personally on digital health services. Republicans have signaled their interest in reducing FDA review of smartphone applications. Moreover, the new administration's policies increase the urgency for lower-cost solutions to deliver care – including more predictive analytics to make sense of healthcare data, more telehealth, and more artificial intelligence. For entrepreneurs driving towards Medicare-driven profits, the anticipated funding cuts over the next several years may call for strategic rethinking.

Insurance Companies – Bottom Line Prediction of TrumpCare Grade: "A+"

(What can we do for you, Mr. Insurance Company?)
We predict that the insurance companies will be the overwhelming winners of the ACA repeal and the emergence of a tax credit driven world. Payment structures will favor them. The push toward wider use of global capitation in MA programs will benefit them. The powers they will gain in the marketplace structure that is apparently part of the Ryan agenda will benefit them. Even without multi-state plans, insurers will gain the ability to

offer narrow networks and provide LC/LB plans with anticipated large margins.

In essence, the ACA tried to push true insurance structure onto healthcare; making everyone play, requiring robust benefit levels, and setting up the ground rules for exchanges, including marketing and risk corridors, and the like, none of which a government has any special expertise in doing. In repealing the ACA, the Trump administration will be returning the business of insurance to the insurers, and they will maximize returns for shareholders. This will lead them to lobby hard for favorable rules like narrow networks and multi-state plans, and will lead them to shift risk to the maximum extent possible off of their books and onto the books of the providers.

We see healthy margins in insurance products that won't be required to offer robust benefits, and will be subject to only minimal state underwriting regulation. With the advent of multi-state plans, no one regulator will have the power it had previously; insurers will undoubtedly forum shop for the most industry-friendly regulators, and establish those friendly jurisdictions as the home base for their multi-state plans.

We also see the Trump administration as being more merger friendly to insurers. Regardless of the outcome of the current merger challenges, we see some additional consolidation among insurers ahead, which will lead to even greater negotiating power. At worst, we see the plans being able to dictate terms and rates to doctors and hospitals because the plans will control the access to the patients, by and large, and because President Trump is handing them the regulatory reins.

NINE:
HOW TRUMPCARE INTERSECTS WITH BROADER FORCES OF HEALTHCARE TRANSFORMATION

In the course of the discussion of the shift from ObamaCare to TrumpCare, it's easy to lose sight of the fact that legislative changes and government regulations are only one of several factors at work simultaneously in the transformation of U.S. healthcare. We are so used to listening to politicians promise how they are going to fix healthcare that we ignore the elephant in the room: the economic, technologic, biological, and structural forces at work in healthcare are much more powerful than the government's limited toolbox to take them on.

The ACA was a significant improvement in healthcare access for millions of Americans, even while it had many detractors and shortcomings.

Sometimes, these forces wreak havoc. The Zika virus or some other public health crisis makes its way around the world, forcing the government and the healthcare system to adapt to a new threat. And the structural rise in employment around the world as an outgrowth of technology, causing economic disruption.

Sometimes, the driving forces of change can be positive. Technology opens up unimagined possibilities, making care more accessible and cheaper. Private industry, more sensitive to profit opportunities and competitive threats, moves much more quickly than government – making concepts into realities on the ground in the process. The story of innovation is often about what people do with other people's ideas. Think Steve Jobs visiting Xerox PARC and seizing ways to exploit technology that Xerox was not prepared to pursue. On a recent trip to Israel, a successful digital health entrepreneur shared a story of this process: he toured an industry giant's innovation lab, and was blown away by its high concept vision of next generation medical devices that were years and probably about a decade away. Returning home with Jobs-like impatience, he hunkered down with a doctor and software engineer for weeks, which turned into months. Through relentless and obsessive focus, they created a prototype of a next generation technology that the rest of the industry was still dreaming of.

Good and bad, these forces are very much alive in healthcare. In this chapter, we consider the way that unrelated forces of change around healthcare are likely to mediate TrumpCare, and vice versa.

Evolving Patient Demands: Consumerism and Care

Although we've been using the timeline of the past 50 years for much of this book, in many ways, patients today, both on an individual level and collectively, are quite different from the patients of even 20 years ago.

Individually, patients today are more well-informed and more demanding in their expectations. It was just a decade ago that we were speaking about U.S. healthcare going from being doctor-driven to a patient- or consumer-centric model. It was only two decades ago, in 1996, that WebMD began enabling consumers to go online and investigate diagnoses. Doctors have had to learn to adapt to patients showing up to appointments armed with information gathered on Google and elsewhere, empowered for the first time to look for second opinions, question doctors' advice, and advocate aggressively for themselves.

The transition continues, and now the term is not just consumer-centered care, but consumer-directed care. Consumers expect to be in control of their healthcare choices. We are living through a time when consumers are beginning to have access to data to assess providers, cutting through the opacity of healthcare pricing and quality, and to question their care.

This trend is part of a broader societal shift of radically greater expectations of choice today. The option to watch content on demand from hundreds of channels or to order your coffee 36 different ways at Starbucks have altered expectations of choice across all consumer markets. Healthcare has been a relative hold-out in terms of letting people make choices about who, when, and where to get care. One of the biggest complaints about ObamaCare was that it actually worsened the options by incentivizing health plans to narrow their networks to fewer numbers of doctors in the interest of reducing costs.

Along with radical expansion of choice, the interrelated shift has been the convenience of constant communication. Our teenage children cannot imagine what life was like when we had to schedule plans with other people without cell phones to let them know we were running late or when we arrived. Younger workers cannot imagine how businesses functioned before we could transmit information instantaneously by email and text, and had to route paper copies. The expectations of convenience constantly ratchet up: why would I call a taxi when Uber lets me press a button on my smartphone and have a car there in minutes without talking to anyone? Why should I look at a map to navigate when Waze offers me real-time traffic-optimized directions that tell me exactly when I will arrive?

On the surface, these developments have nothing to do with healthcare. But they cause consumers to question why they aren't getting the same level of convenience in other aspects of their lives. Healthcare has consistently been in the rear guard of convenience despite consumer demands. Whether online or in brick-and-mortar settings, patients who once settled for long waits in dreary institutional doctor's offices are restless for more convenience in healthcare, and U.S. healthcare is still not there. The patients of tomorrow will demand the ability to eliminate the inconveniences of paperwork, long waits, and traditional phone scheduling via digital solutions. In the words of cardiologist Dr. Eric Topol's book title, the era of "The doctor will see you now" has been replaced with the era of "The Patient Will See You Now."

> *Healthcare has consistently been in the rear guard of convenience despite consumer demands.*

Some skeptics question whether these trends of choice and convenience are only relevant to a small segment of healthcare consumers at the top of the market and not to everyone else. While it's true that more disposable income translates to more economic power to make healthcare choices, there are signs that the trend is not just limited to high income patients. The focus today is meeting all patients where they are. Big retailers like Walmart and CVS, eyeing growth opportunities, have already taken note of how inconvenient healthcare is and seized on opportunities by opening retail clinics (in Walmart's case, for its employees and customers, and, of course, the CVS Minute Clinic). These are just early leaders as retailers explore how they can capitalize on their skill at delivering choice and convenience to capture healthcare dollars. Many health systems are heeding the same call, as evidenced by the proliferation of smaller retail locations, ending the era of patients needing to come to a big hospital for everything. While lower and middle income patients will experience the benefits later than high income patients, the trend will ultimately transform healthcare.

What does this trend portend for TrumpCare and how will TrumpCare affect this trend? While the driving force is social and cultural change range than government-driven change, there is a synergy between the Republican move to market-driven healthcare. As we explored in Chapter 4, the Republican vision to shrink the role of health insurance and put people in charge of how they spend their healthcare dollars aligns with this trend. In place of public frustration over insurance companies narrowing their networks and limiting patient choices, TrumpCare gives power to the people. Ironically, the people who voted against President Trump for fear of what he would do to healthcare may end up being the biggest beneficiaries of a newfound leverage to demand healthcare the way they want it.

In place of public frustration over insurance companies narrowing their networks and limiting patient choices, TrumpCare gives power to the people.

The Virtues of Underinsurance?

Beyond consumer expectations, a practical reality for patients today is the widespread challenge of underinsurance (high out-of-pocket cost relative to income). While the Affordable Care Act expanded access to care, the concomitant erosion of the value of health insurance benefits and increasing costs of care meant that, even with health insurance, many patients were in a worse position to afford their share of personal responsibility for deductibles, co-payments, and uncovered expenses. A higher percentage of people are at risk of not being able to afford the care they need in the event of a crisis. Patient underinsurance has the potential to drive a new finance market, as consumers look to borrow money to spread out healthcare costs they want or need over time – as an alternative to insurance.

While the Republican vision may not solve the problem of underinsurance for healthcare disasters, it may provide a "silver lining" in driving more market-driven pricing. Today's healthcare prices remain inflated, in part because healthcare providers develop their pricing strategies to maximize reimbursement from insurance companies. This leads to multiple problems. Leaving aside the question of whether third-party payment leads to overutilization because patients aren't bearing the expense, the byzantine nature of insurance reimbursement incentivizes healthcare providers (at least in the out-of-network context) to set their prices as high as insurance might pay, and then to wait to see what the insurance companies actually pay. In recent years, insurance companies have increasingly accused healthcare providers (such as surgery centers and addiction treatment programs) of committing fraud if they utilize one price for insurance purposes and a lower cash price for patients. The virtue of removing insurance from the equation for non-catastrophic care is that, without insurance, pricing will go where consumers are willing to pay.

In Chapter 7, we alluded to the trend of direct care, meaning cash-pay medicine where the patient pays the doctor directly for medical services. The doctor does not accept insurance, although in some cases, if the patients want to bill insurance themselves, they can try. Doctors can charge on a pay per visit model, with an all-inclusive annual fee (as many concierge doctors do), or some combination of annual fee, and a charge per visit – sort of like a gym membership. Direct care has grown, as exemplified by primary care providers like MedLion and by small box retail providers of chiropractic and other kinds of care. These types of services are poised to grow because they give people what they want and are transparently priced to meet the out-of-pocket budgets of patients.

The Force of the Silver Tsunami

Perhaps the biggest change in the U.S. healthcare market is the predominance of senior patients. The aging of America is a game-changer for healthcare. The "old old" (over age 85) have become the fastest growing population segment in the country. The "Silver Tsunami" has begun as the oldest Baby Boomers hit Medicare eligibility age and the rest will join the ranks of Medicare over the next two decades. This explosion of the senior population will drive spending, as chronic diseases (and diseases of prosperity) associated with aging (i.e., cancer, heart disease, diabetes) affect a larger percentage of the population. It will drive the growth of Medicare-covered services as well as the market for non-covered services, as more and more people will need help with activities of daily living.

> *Perhaps the biggest change in the U.S. healthcare market is the predominance of senior patients.*

While Republican focus is on Medicaid expense, in light of the aging population, the real challenge of the future of government spending on healthcare is Medicare costs. In this regard, TrumpCare and the shift to more focus on direct out-of-pocket payment for healthcare, through HSAs or otherwise, will be a good thing. For example, the biggest savings opportunities may be in getting patients and families to understand that they will need to cover the costs of homecare attendants, and that access to Medicare-funded services (such as home health agencies) are reserved for limited episodes of serious, unexpected needs.

The Technology-Driven Digital Health Revolution

In addition to changing patient expectations and demographic shifts, new care delivery models are also a driving force of change. The growth of digital healthcare, for example, is not merely a matter of meeting patient convenience expectations, but a significant shift to technology, data-driven care, and connectivity enabling a growing number of more straightforward conditions to be treated seamlessly via healthcare information technology.

As wearable technologies and smartphone diagnostic tools improve, patients are better positioned to identify and manage their own health issues in a radically more efficient manner than the days of visiting doctors for basic diagnostic tests. Doctors are just beginning to rely on patient-reported or smart-phone gathered cardiopulmonary vitals to prescribe medications.

The next generation of telehealth solutions will be increasingly streamlined and focused on increasing and improving quality data sources, driving changes in the standard of care across a wide range of specialized health services. In the process, many minor health problems will be resolved with electronically-delivered prescriptions, which patients can have filled online and delivered without visiting pharmacies. The online video telehealth appointment won't supplant the in-person visit for complex conditions, but the ability to snap photos of skin lesions for diagnosis and prescribing and to get more straightforwardly diagnosable conditions treated remotely represents a care delivery model that is going to grow in popularity and the scope of available treatments.

Beyond smartphones and wearable technology, the ability to monitor bedridden patients through new telemonitoring technologies and the ability of devices to transmit data (connected via "the Internet of Things") to remote healthcare providers means that patients will no longer need to travel as frequently to the doctor's office to check their blood pressure, blood sugar, or other indicators. This, in turn, will enable doctors (or increasingly, nurses) to review the collected data, check in with patients, and provide clinical feedback via a telehealth encounter, focusing the need for actual in-person visits on home care to provide help with activities of daily living. While many of the current devices require human input to confirm data prior to transmission, the next generation of telemonitoring will detect data with increasing automation.

Another powerful role of telemonitoring will be to provide early warning signs, such as changes in blood pressure resulting from a blockage, before a heart attack. Doctors can anticipate potential problems and respond before the damage is done, scheduling procedures or directing them to hospitals before a life-threatening event. This process will reduce mortality risks and offer the opportunity for more intensive intervention at home to avoid readmission when preventable. Other opportunities combine new nanotechnology solutions that expand diagnostic opportunities with advances in artificial intelligence (AI) – the "smartening" of healthcare devices for an increasing array of tasks, using data analysis tools to refine and calibrate decision-making. Future generation of devices will feature the improving ability to talk, listen, see, recognize, and ultimately, make decisions via pattern recognition and "cognitive" computing.

In thinking about the failure of ObamaCare and the prospects of TrumpCare to reduce healthcare costs and improve care, it is arguable that TrumpCare is a better fit for these technologies. One unintended consequence of insurance coverage was that it diminished the need for people to reach into their own wallets to pay for care. As amazing as the available telehealth resources are, the biggest impediment to adoption has been the reluctance of patients to pay out of pocket. As a result, several of the largest telehealth providers nationally have struggled in recent years and undergone leadership changes in search of profitability.

With a "skinnier" scope of insurance coverage and patients incentivized to use their HSAs, TrumpCare is likely to spur more patient spending. This would not only help turn around the underutilization of the largest providers in the market today, but further expand the market for new applications of telehealth.

Just as TrumpCare will be good for consumer-focused digital health, these technologies will be good for TrumpCare. After all, nothing holds out the promise of improved quality and reduced costs more than technology. It is little wonder the President Trump is proposing to enable more health-related smartphone apps to bypass FDA approval altogether.

> Just as TrumpCare will be good for consumer-focused digital health, these technologies will be good for TrumpCare.

Greater Return on Investment in Biomedical Research and Health Informatics

Apart from the changing landscape of healthcare service delivery, an enormous part of the transformation is occurring in life sciences and healthcare information technology (IT). Ongoing advances in biomedical research, in combination with health informatics, are driving toward an unprecedented level of precision in medical care and generally greater ROI in healthcare treatment.

The revolution is apparent in research and treatment of cancer, neurologic and cardiac disease, and study of the human genome. Biomedical research is driving significant progress in scientific understanding of the brain, the microbiome, the nervous system, and other less understood parts of our physiology, which is expected to produce a host of new and more cost effective treatments, medications, and biologic agents. The next several years will be a time of new diagnostic tests, new therapies, and the ability to personalize care. For example, by understanding a patient's DNA (or RNA) sequence, providers can assess the existing genetic variations that can account for possible diseases, and assess how that patient will likely respond to a certain treatment. With this level of personalized information, diagnostics, and therapeutics, there will be less investment in costly treatments that ultimately fail.

Health informatics, the use of IT and healthcare data acquisition and analysis to improve the quality and safety of patient care, will be a driver of opportunities as well. The capacity to amass, organize, and analyze voluminous amounts of health data is driving a growing body of analytics that can be used to manage population health on a broad scale. These same tools also support individual healthcare decision-making on diagnosis and treatment. As a result, many healthcare problems will be diagnosed and treated more effectively, and the most difficult problems will benefit from "crowdsourcing," (i.e., more efficient problem-solving that leverages everyone everywhere with value to contribute).

The life science industry is expected to produce many new therapies and therapeutic devices in coming years, including applications of simulated experience through virtual reality (VR) for treatment of health conditions. Therapeutic VR aligns with numerous trends in healthcare, including the shift towards lower-cost, convenient, consumer-directed care. VR is expected to produce tools to manage anxiety and depression, provide neurocognitive support for recovery from addiction, improve weight loss effectiveness, mitigate post-traumatic stress disorder, and support other behavioral health conditions. VR also holds promise as a training tool for consumers (on wellness and disease prevention) and health professionals (for simulated training ranging from primary care medicine to advanced surgeries).

Robotic medical technologies are also expected to lead strong medical device growth in the years ahead, including a growing range of technologies that enhance human performance. Robotic technologies are not only transforming life directly for patients, but also changing how care is delivered, from surgical robots used for minimally-invasive procedures to robotic prescription dispensing systems. One big frontier ahead is the extension of robotics into "micro-bots," tiny robots injected into the human body to perform a function, such as to confirm a diagnosis, perform an operative procedure, or deliver of a therapeutic agent to a particular site. Robotics also hold promise for infection control and other healthcare problems where the risk of human error presents continued challenges.

As we discussed in Chapter 5, the Trump administration will inherit a burst of new funding for precision medicine through the 21st Century Cures Act. While these innovations are driven by scientific progress irrespective of the political winds, we expect TrumpCare to be supportive of funding these efforts and facilitating regulatory processes to take advantage of new science. The only point of divergence is likely to be the issue we described in Chapter 5, of President Trump's quest for better deals on pricey biotech.

"Outpatientification"

As noted above, patients today expect healthcare providers to meet them where they are, limiting visits to the big hospitals to situations that need that level of care. Even as the needs for higher acuity care in our aging and sick population have increased, the pressure to minimize expensive inpatient hospital and post-acute (nursing home) stays are driving people to lower acuity settings and growing use of "extensivists," physicians focused on keeping people out of hospitals and in assisted living or outpatient care settings. Residential care settings, such as assisted living facilities, have seen an increasing level of acuity in the conditions they are expected to manage. In the social services arena, SWAT teams of case managers and mental health professionals, in partnership with physicians, are keeping more people out of psychiatric hospitalizations. Non-medical detox options for drug overdoses are growing in popularity, in lieu of hospitalizations.

The most radical alternative care setting ahead is the "hospital-at-home" trend, made possible by telemonitoring and home support services. Patients and families prefer to return home to convalesce rather than transition to impersonal, institutional settings, aligning with government and payer interest in reduced cost. This convergence of interests, coupled with growing technological support, is expected to fuel a driving trend of convalescing at home, with shorter hospital stays and at a lower cost.

> As in the case of technology, the trend of "outpatientification" may fit more naturally in TrumpCare than it did under ObamaCare as a value-driven, free market solution.

The Growing Role of Non-Physician Professionals

Physician shortages and cost factors have driven greater dependence on non-physician professionals – physician assistants (PAs), nurse practitioners (NPs), and other advance practice nurses (APRNs) – to provide primary care services. In many states, nurse practitioners have full practice authority to operate independently of physicians. This model is breaking into new frontiers where physicians now predominate, such as long-term care. Nurse midwives are a rising force in delivering babies. The different profile of the non-physician health professional workforce of the future may be an important downward driver of healthcare costs, aligning with a key Republican goal.

Predictive Data Analytics

Perhaps the biggest force ahead in reshaping healthcare will be data analytics. Data analytics enables a way of managing the health of entire populations, rather than individual patients. By using data analytics and machine learning to build predictive models, healthcare systems will be able to flag warning signs and high-risk events, among other things. In many cases, the reason healthcare costs so much is that we deal with problems too late. Early intervention holds out the hope of using lower cost therapies and changing patient behaviors before "the train comes off the rails" with a heart attack, stroke, or other event.

> *Perhaps the biggest force ahead in reshaping healthcare will be data analytics.*

The value of analytics also holds out the promise of a sharp reduction in fraud and abuse through the shift from our current "pay and chase" model healthcare reimbursement (in which payers automatically pay billed claims and only later audit and seek repayment or recoupment of overpaid amounts). Government programs and private insurers alike will seek pre-authorization and demonstration of medical necessity and documentation in advance to authorize payment of claims. This will be accompanied by growing reliance on the predictive analytics and data-mining tools utilized by the credit card industry to quickly identify aberrational data through algorithms, reducing fraud, waste, and abuse.

The Grim Implications of Technology on Jobs

While we believe that health technology will be a force for good, we feel compelled to raise a darker aspect of technological progress. The same power that portends higher quality, lower cost care also points to the disappearance of jobs. While the 2016 election focused on blaming China and other culprits for the loss of high-paying U.S. industrial jobs, there was no discussion of the real issue: jobs are disappearing faster than moving overseas as the result of technology. The same processes in robotics and machine learning that enable remote patient monitoring and care are driving this trend. And the problem is going to get much worse in coming decades, not better.

Short of a global Luddite revolution to destroy all computer technology, governments and political leaders have no answers. The good jobs that so many people are counting on Donald Trump to bring back are never coming back. They represent a bygone era. Instead, the future holds steadily rising unemployment. The next wave of people to see their jobs disappear will be the middle managers, who aren't needed in a world of more artificial intelligence, data analytics, and online marketplaces. We are heading toward previously unheard of rates of structural unemployment approaching or exceeding 20%.

What does this mean for the future of healthcare? It points to a widening gap where a higher percentage of people will be displaced and need social support: not just healthcare, but housing, social support, and retraining for the different kinds of jobs of the future. It also points to the problem of any purely private market solution: there are going to be many more Americans in need of public assistance ahead.

What does this mean for the future of healthcare? It points to a widening gap where a higher percentage of people will be displaced and need social support.

Industry Realignment, Consolidation, and Evolving Competitive Landscape

Beyond the way that evolutions in consumer behavior and innovation in healthcare products and services drive change, broader economic forces are also a force in transforming healthcare. Both the changes "on the ground" in healthcare and government directives (of which the ACA is only part of the story) have put pressure on the business models of many health plans, systems, and providers. In some cases, changing financial arrangements strained existing business models. As just one example, Kindred Healthcare, the largest post-acute healthcare provider in the country, announced that it was closing all of its skilled nursing facilities (SNFs). Just a few years ago, Kindred operated over 300 SNFs, and within a few years it will be out of the business. This kind of change is emblematic of the way that healthcare companies are pivoting, looking to exit declining business lines and move towards growth areas. A new competitive environment emerges as old players realign and new entrants disrupt the existing healthcare marketplace.

Realignment is not simply about individual companies choosing their own trajectories, but also a broader trend towards consolidation, as the new landscape demands greater scale for financial sustainability. In the past 15 years, for example, the model that predominated physician practices in 50 years ago – small and solo practice – has been whittled away. The vast majority of physicians today practice in larger, hospital-affiliated groups.

For different reasons, hospitals are likewise consolidating, leaving smaller, independent operators at a disadvantage. As the economics of hospital business operations change, for example, through the suppression of hospital admissions and changing reimbursement rules, hospitals that were profitable five years ago find themselves barely at break-even. Institutions who were at break-even find themselves losing money. The changing reimbursement landscape has made size, scale, and leverage necessities for profitability. Significant consolidation is expected to broaden across additional healthcare sectors, including post-acute and home health agencies.

Amidst these forces, as noted above, non-healthcare businesses pursuing opportunities in the healthcare marketplace, either as new entrants or in partnership with existing healthcare companies, are a disruptive force. Beyond larger retailers like Walmart, drug stores, spas, food companies, apparel makers, gyms, and wellness companies are exploring opportunities. These efforts not only respond to consumer-driven demand, but also present the challenge of competition for the existing market players.

How do these changes affect TrumpCare and how will it affect them? Through ACOs and other initiatives, ObamaCare sought to incentivize collaborations between existing providers to share risk and coordinate care. While the Republicans have expressed misgivings about particular ACA initiatives, the trend toward coordinated care is a shared goal and is likely to accelerate, with a greater role for care managers who coordinate patient needs comprehensively across settings, making sure that patients are treated efficiently and seamlessly. TrumpCare will share ObamaCare's goals of reducing duplicative diagnostics, ensuring access to information about what other providers are doing, and simultaneously improving the quality of care and reducing fraud, waste, and abuse.

Implications of Structural Forces

Whether TrumpCare embraces all of the forces above or not, they are a big part of the story of healthcare transformation. Ultimately, government can set rules that incentivize the kinds of behavior that it wants to see. The Trump administration will make decisions about science and medical funding, regulating Internet medicine, and other markets could speed up or hinder this transformation. At the end of the day, though, social, technological, and economic waves of change end up being far more determinative of how our system transforms.

> *Ultimately, government can set rules that incentivize the kinds of behavior that it wants to see.*

When the history of this era of U.S. healthcare is written (with slightly more distance and perspective than this book allowed), it is likely that the story of ObamaCare and TrumpCare will supply the drama. The story is still unfolding in front of us. But the conflict between Republicans and Democrats is likely to be a sideshow and not the central narrative arc. This reality should offer some comfort to people who are disconsolate about the impact of the changeover from ObamaCare to TrumpCare.

TEN:
BIG QUESTIONS AHEAD: WHERE DO WE GO FROM HERE?

For most of this book, we've been talking about the healthcare future in terms of the next 4 or 8 years. Our goal in this chapter is to offer a longer-term perspective about how the problems and potential solutions in healthcare are likely to play out, and what might be done differently to fix U.S. healthcare. As with much of our story, it's a good new-bad news combination.

The good news is that the worst is unlikely. For readers who came to this book seriously worried about losing their healthcare coverage and what comes after the repeal of ObamaCare, we hope that our predictions about the way that politics, public opinion, and Democratic opposition are likely to play out – including the unlikelihood that millions of Americans will lose newly gained health coverage – afford some measure of comfort. As the election itself showed, there are no sure things in American politics. Still, we don't believe that President Trump will allow his legacy to be the guy who took away healthcare coverage from 20 million people.

For readers who picked up this book depressed about the

Republicans undoing all of the progress (beyond expanding access to care) that ObamaCare yielded, we hope that this book has offered some reasons to take a closer look. As a clumsy set of compromises, there were more than a few areas where the ACA did not work, and where Republican market-driven reforms may actually do some good and align more effectively with the structural forces transforming healthcare, like consumer expectations, the aging population, and technology. If Republican reforms make inroads into tackling problems that ObamaCare did not fix – such as moderating the rising cost of healthcare – that would be good news. We also see room for a measure of optimism in remembering – without minimizing the precarious possibilities – that one set of government policies or another are just a small piece of the bigger story of U.S. healthcare.

Medicaid's Original Sin

So what's the bad news? Where do we begin? Let's start with the Medicaid expansion. We don't need to wait for a Medicaid rollback for more bad news. If you are living at or near federal poverty level in a Medicaid hold-out state, you're already in trouble. The gap between healthcare haves and have-nots is widening, and living where you do makes you a second-class citizen when it comes to healthcare.

As you may have inferred, we consider the lingering second-class status that the Medicaid program has had since its inception to be a serious, unresolved problem. Under the heading of "if you are going to do something, do it right," it is almost hard to watch how the Medicaid program was set up to fail in comparison to Medicare. It is little wonder that conservatives and progressives share a desire to wash their hands of Medicaid, albeit with opposite end goals. From the beginning, it has been feared, underfunded, and administered unevenly.

This has been a longtime problem, but we believe it will get worse as economic and healthcare disparities continue to widen within the United States thanks to the structural forces of rising unemployment that we address in Chapter 9 with more Americans out of work and earning less. It's time to reconsider the strategy behind the deliberate disparity in how we treat low income and senior Americans.

As we discuss in Chapter 2, ObamaCare and Congressional Democrats made the logical and politically viable choice to expand Medicaid, knowing that a universal Medicare plan, which Bernie Sanders advocated for in the 2016 campaign, would have been politically dead on arrival. The Sanders proposal is what progressives want to see as the Democratic platform going forward: the consolidation of Medicare and Medicaid into one program of universal Medicare for the old, the disabled, and the poor.

We see the idea of universal Medicare as unlikely ever to win over pragmatic moderate Democrats, let alone Republicans, because of the high cost of doing so, even though it would solve some serious problems. Does it make sense, for example, for an advanced society like ours, to leave healthcare access to the whims of personal fortune? Do we want a system in which people are left to win either the genetic lottery (i.e., high income parents) or the job market lottery, in order to get good access to healthcare? Are we prepared simply to sigh "c'est la vie" to the barriers to healthcare for everyone else? That doesn't sound right for a country as charitable and wealthy as ours. So what do we do?

Polarized Politics as an Impediment to Fixing Healthcare
Fixing U.S. healthcare boils down to two things: first, rectifying the disparity in access to the world's best system of

healthcare providers, and, second, finding a way to make the whole thing affordable, both within the national budget and for any particular individual. In political terms, fixing healthcare should begin with mediating between serious liberal and conservative visions to find consensus and to negotiate political compromise.

> *Fixing U.S. healthcare boils down to two things: first, rectifying the disparity in access to the world's best system of healthcare providers, and, second, finding a way to make the whole thing affordable, both within the national budget and for any particular individual.*

Unfortunately, there is little chance of that happening anytime soon. Republicans flatly rejected ObamaCare's approach and now promise to undo it. After all, Democrats had their chance to impose their will for eight years; now Republican get a turn. What do we expect when the next Democratic president is elected or when Democrats take back Congress? And when Republicans do so again after that? The parties cycle back and forth: three steps forward, two steps back. ObamaCare. Trump Care. What next? For readers who were depressed about the way that our political system is unable to deal with the complex public policy challenge of healthcare, welcome to the club.

We are so far from consensus on healthcare today that, almost by definition, any change occurs under protest of the political opposition, setting up a destabilizing cycle. Looking back to the real chance that President Nixon and Senator Kennedy had in the early 1970s, which we touch on in Chapter 2, to reach compromise and fix America's healthcare gaps, it is depressing to think about where we stand today. What will it take just to get to a political climate where we can break through the status quo and begin a serious conversation about healthcare?

A Call to Action

Since we are living through a time when our political leaders seem unable or unwilling to have a constructive dialogue about, let alone negotiate, the issues that America needs to work through to fix healthcare, it is incumbent on all of us to take on that work. Instead of playing into cycle of villainizing the other side and allowing politicians to get away with fuzzy promises to make things better based on one-sided plans, we need to be the ones asking the hard questions. We need to begin speaking openly and honestly about the enormous challenges ahead for U.S. healthcare.

We offer this book not as the last word, but as an opening, an invitation to a new conversation, a dialogue that is open-minded, that asks critical questions compassionately and is not just limited in to siloed communities of the like-minded (and economically aligned). We need to talk about healthcare with serious people who see things differently than we do. We need a movement that crosses party lines and abandons the ideology and cynicism in search of a hopeful, inclusive vision to fix what's broken in U.S. healthcare.

> *We need a movement that crosses party lines and abandons the ideology and cynicism in search of a hopeful, inclusive vision to fix what's broken in U.S. healthcare.*

What are the things that our political leaders don't want to or can't talk about? Powerful lobbies and divisive politics have made it politically suicidal to talk about limiting certain kinds of public spending on care. When the ACA created the IPAB, for example, to rein in spending, some Republicans branded it a "death panel" intended to ration healthcare. This label was memorably colorful, but illustrates not only how to shut down dialogue, but how to delegitimize the other side in the process. There is a need for a real conversations about how to contain spending (as IPAB set out to do), and also to talk about how much certain kinds of care costs, about who is going to pay the bill, and about whether certain kinds of expenditures are not in the public interest. Are there treatments that public funding will cover for 50-year-olds but not for 80-year olds? Where, for example, do we draw the line on invasive measures (such as expensive cancer care) for people who are plainly nearing the end of life? Do we simply try to persuade people to consider dying with more dignity and focusing on quality, rather than quantity of life when the end is close? Or do we actively impose limits on what government funding will cover?

There are an endless array of these questions. Should public funding be used for invasive treatment of lung cancer in a lifelong smoker? People who have the resources to pay can keep their loved ones on life support eternally if that is their wish, but we as a society need to be able to say, "This is what we pay for, and this is what we don't." At the same time, we have to address the fear of government bureaucrats armed with big data prescribing what's right for individual patients under a "we're paying for it, so we get to decide what your doctor does" approach. Unfortunately, in a polarized environment, politicians can't have hard conversations that raise uncomfortable questions. That means that the rest of us need to have these conversations.

Beyond the details, there are difficult conversations we need to be having about bigger questions. How much healthcare inequality are we willing to tolerate based on income? If we were designing a system from scratch, for example, what kind of care would public funds pay for, and what kinds of care would only be available based on ability to pay? At the present time, we avoid questions like these altogether.

More fundamentally, do we believe that healthcare is a right or basic need like public education? Alternatively, is it a privilege? What are the implications of our positions on this issue?

There are series of deeper questions underlying the ambivalence towards Medicaid: to what extent are U.S. attitudes driven by misgivings about the nature of poverty itself, including perspectives that people are poor as a matter of divine will or that people are poor because they're lazy? To what extent are we willing to put limits on "I've got mine" selfishness?

There are tough questions to be asked about personal accountability. In Chapter 1, we addressed the six 'S's' that clinicians identify as a large part of the problem of healthcare cost and the gap between the U.S. and the rest of the developed world. Why has no liberal politician in the past eight years of "patient-centric care" prominently suggested that the fault lies in the mirror of every house in America? How do we address the challenge of political exposure outweighing courage for candidates standing for election?

How much are we willing to allow the market to drive healthcare availability, and when do we intervene to address market defects like pricing when a single drug has no competition? Market defects in healthcare have been abundant. Just to pick on one, consider the case of William McGuire, UnitedHealthcare's CEO in the early 2000s. McGuire paid himself a bonus approaching $2 billion (with a "b") dollars. He hadn't invented anything or cured any disease; he was just a steward for financial assets for shareholders and beneficiaries. Yes, he backdated some stock option grants to obtain this money, so there were ethical issues that led to his resignation. But the larger point is that maybe insurers, who in an insurance system are supposed to bear risk, are rewarded by the capital markets for avoiding risk, which gives rise to an inherent conflict and structural difficulty when it comes to healthcare.

What do we do about insurance? Does insurance inflate healthcare costs? (We think it does.) What would be the implications of eliminating health insurance companies altogether or limiting insurance, as we do in other contexts, to catastrophes?

Perhaps the hardest conversations relate to global trends that portend greater economic disparity and an even greater need for public funding of healthcare in the future. As we describe in Chapter 9, we worry that we managed to get through a presidential election that focused on lost American jobs, but largely ignored the structural forces that not only have taken those jobs, but will take many more. The voter anger that both President Trump and Bernie Sanders harnessed flows from this, though none of our candidates was willing to level with voters and address the hard truth: no matter how well President Trump negotiates and no matter how tough we get on fair trade, these efforts amount to spitting into the wind against the larger economic forces driving up structural unemployment rates worldwide.

The real issue isn't China but the power of machine learning and robotics, which threaten not just industrial jobs, but middle management and professional services as well. Since our political leaders are afraid to talk about it, it's on all of us to level with people about the future and have a real conversation about what we are going to do when unemployment doubles and maybe even quadruples from where it stands today. We need to talk about what we're willing to do for the dislocated -- on healthcare and other social support -- and what we need to keep our social fabric from tearing further.

The questions that need to be asked and answered in respectful, pluralistic conversations go on and on. On many of these questions, we have opinions that we've expressed or hinted at throughout this book, but that doesn't preclude our desire – and need – to engage with opposing views.

Until we begin to have real conversations, we remain stuck in a bad movie, where we know what's coming next and are forced to watch it unfold painfully in front of us.

Meanwhile, our healthcare problems remain unaddressed or they worsen, as is the case with widening socioeconomic disparities. Both sides do not seem to see the other side's complaints as problems, which in and of itself is part of the problem.

Compromising to Fix Healthcare

Where might real discussions and political compromise lead us to fix healthcare? As noted above, there are two distinct problems: disparity in access and affordability. There is no one path to address these issues, only better and worse options. Since political compromise is off the table for now, we may as well consider the spectrum of possibilities that would be available if we wiped the healthcare slate clean. Even if many of the single payer and universal coverage models out there are too progressive to be politically viable in the U.S. at this moment in time, they offer ideas that could be retooled and "Americanized."

Solving disparity in access to care begins with universal coverage. We can and must get beyond the question of whether poor people should be covered in the first place. Beyond the ACA's model of expanding Medicaid and the individual mandate, we should be exploring multiple other options. One model, for example, would be to set individual share of cost according to income level.

This is a feature of Singapore's system: a national health system that utilizes a means-tested system of subsidized self-insurance. Singaporeans receive a subsidy proportionate to their income, but everyone pays something out of pocket. Singapore uses mandatory savings through payroll deductions to pay for the national system, which are tracked in personally tracked "Medisave" accounts, and which also fund insurance for people who cannot afford their healthcare expenses. People are required to carry catastrophic insurance, but elect whether or not to buy other private health insurance or to utilize private, out-of-pocket medical care.

Our point is not to suggest that Singapore presents the solution to U.S. problems. Instead, it exemplifies a potential compromise: maximizing personal accountability and efficiency with private accounts while ensuring that financial wherewithal is not a barrier to care. Models like this one could be a useful starting point for thinking about a different approach to U.S. healthcare that addresses liberal concerns about fairness and conservative concerns about enabling market forces to serve their role.

Making healthcare more affordable also presents many options. In Chapter 4, we touched on several market-driven solutions, like narrowing the scope of insurance and expanding out-of-pocket spending to create pressure for efficient pricing. It would be valuable to explore models that employ this feature, as well as options on the spectrum between the extremes of purely catastrophic coverage and coverage of routine care.

One catalyst for change might be employers. Insurance companies are increasingly pushing employers toward some form of self-insured status. Rather than managing the healthcare buy, most employers would likely be happy to cede the acquisition and management of healthcare to a governmental organization or other entity, and just pay a tax. After all, many employees are uncomfortable about their employers having so much control over their healthcare and being locked into their jobs because of their health coverage, an issue the ACA tried to address.

To explore this model, we suggest consideration of the German model: employer payroll taxes (and personal income taxes) fund the system, but individuals choose from competing "sickness plans" that offer a government-defined benefit under a universal insurance mandate. High income individuals can elect to buy out of the mandate with a more expensive, optional secondary layer of private insurance. A future American universal coverage might consider a version of this model as a way not simply to shift the model of employer care, but to end the fragmented approaches to coverage of distinct populations (employees, seniors, the poor, uninsured individuals) and move towards a simplified universal system of coverage.

We acknowledge that, at the moment, it is far-fetched to imagine bipartisan support for scrapping the existing employee- based system. But again, looking at the compromises in other systems may offer ideas for resolving the issues in ours.

These kinds of healthcare compromises are only the tip of the iceberg of reforms around which political compromises could be negotiated. For the time being, though, they remain a pipe dream. What will it take to spur resolution? A public health crisis? A national emergency? Whatever the stimulus, we invite you to join us in continuing to look for avenues to advance the discussions toward a more reliably accessed and affordable system.

Revival of Single Payer: Exploring the Models

Since consensus and compromise are for now off the table, it is worth exploring what the political opposition is likely to support in the next cycle. As the Democratic party begins to look ahead to the 2018 midterm and 2012 presidential elections, it will also need to head back to the drawing board in search of a new consensus on healthcare. The unraveling of the ACA is likely to strengthen the call among progressives in Congress to support a public option to ensure expanded healthcare access.

Ironically, even as Republicans strategy of repeal-and-delay will preserve the ACA status quo for the time being, the Democrats may very well abandon the ACA model, particularly the individual mandate and insurance exchanges. The centrist impulse to compromise that marked the ACA was a failure, as was Hillary Clinton's embrace of the ACA in the November 2016 election.

The secret to engaging the Democratic base may be

Elizabeth Warren and Bernie Sanders leading the charge for single payer. It has the virtue of simplicity, since Medicare is already a single-payer system, albeit one with narrow eligibility. Under the model advocated by Sanders in the 2016 campaign, Medicare would be broadened to universal coverage, covering everybody without employer-based coverage. While Democratic efforts are unlikely to make a difference under a Trump Administration and Republican Congress, we expect the renewed debate to breathe new life into the movement for single payer and to serve as a Democratic rallying cry to mobilize voters in the not-too-distant future.

What does the long-term future hold?

The long-term future of U.S. healthcare, in terms of access and affordability, will look different from ObamaCare and TrumpCare. Ultimately, we will need to address the hard questions and insist upon individual accountability, combined with purchasing controls vested in and financial support provided for all individuals. There is no long-term solution without universal access for at least a common set of minimum services that all people can count on receiving.

How will the U.S. reach consensus on the type of delivery system, the choices it makes, and the investment opportunities it pursues? Having made our share of predictions in this book, we'll dispense with speculation and instead offer some thoughts about the path we'd like to see taken to fix healthcare. There's no one right answer, only a series of choices.

We would like to see a push for affordability by making insurance a smaller piece of the puzzle: mandatory catastrophic health insurance, where low premiums can protect all of us against expensive but rare healthcare interventions, perhaps pharmaceutical insurance, but no more all-encompassing employer-sponsored insurance plans, which are anchoring our broken system.

What we would like to see are open access healthcare facilities and professionals could do. Instead of mixing private insurance, cash payment, and government-funded care the way our current hospitals do, we think the experiment of exclusively government funded facilities (sharing a common information technology (IT) platform) might solve the problems of access and affordability in one fell swoop. In our imagination, open access translates to a whole set of the core kinds of care that people are not getting: obstetrics, ER, trauma, primary care, chronic disease management, preventative medicine, cardiology (not transplant), advanced infectious disease, orthopedic, general surgery, urology, oncology, ophthalmology, and related hospitalization, skilled nursing, and rehabilitation services. Services would be subject to copays for people who could afford to pay, perhaps from HSAs or tax credit accounts.

Beyond that, anyone who wanted to buy elective insurance could do so on the market. But ideally, people would be incentivized to pay for healthcare by spending their own personal funds.

We aren't claiming these ideas are the right answer, only that they are concept we would like to see tested. If they are not solutions, then we can move on to the next experiment.

Let us know what you think, even if it's to tell us why we're wrong. In the process, you'll be adding to the wellspring of national dialogue and debate that we are calling for.

Maybe this dialogue will lead to experimentation with new solutions to the problems of healthcare. Or perhaps they will generate enough pressure on our political leaders that to force out of their ideological silos and convene a nonpartisan, independent forum to address the challenges of fixing healthcare. Or may it will take something more to spur a national campaign to educate the American public about the brokenness of U.S. healthcare and the need for reform.

Is it too outlandish to imagine a widespread movement committed to meeting and overcoming the U.S. healthcare challenge? Are we dreaming when we think that it's possible to move from a dialogue to decision-making, to convene serious thinkers to approach the challenge of national healthcare with diverse perspectives, and emerge with real proposals? Call us crazy. It's been said about other people in this story.

GLOSSARY

CHIP: The State Children's Health Insurance Program, a program administered by HHS that provides matching funds to states for health insurance to uninsured families with children that have incomes too high to qualify for Medicaid.

CMMI: The Center for Medicare & Medicaid Innovation, an entity created by the ACA, supports (with CMS) the development and testing of innovative healthcare payment and service delivery models.

CMS: The Center for Medicare and Medicaid Services; the bureau of the US Department of Health and Human Services that runs the Medicare program and dictates who healthcare is delivered to in US hospitals.

COBRA: The Consolidated Omnibus Budget Reconciliation Act of 1985 is the law that requires employers to allow employees to continue health insurance coverage after leaving.

EMTALA: The Emergency Medical Treatment and Labor Act (EMTALA), the law that requires ERs to treat and stabilize patients irrespective of ability to pay.

ER: An emergency room at a U.S. hospital where at least one physician trained in emergency medicine is on duty and where any member of the public may enter to receive care.

ERISA: The Employee Retirement Income Security Act of 1974, the law that establishes the rules for large employer, self-funded health (and other) benefit plans, exempting them from state requirements.

HCFA: The Health Care Finance Administration, which began overseeing the Medicare program in 1977. Renamed CMS in 2001.

Health plans: The insurance companies and the coverage that they sell to employers and individuals which obligates them to pay healthcare providers for care to patients.

Healthcare providers: The entities and individuals that deliver healthcare services and products to patients. We use the term to include doctors and other health professionals, hospitals and other health facilities, and life sciences companies that provide drugs and medical devices.

HHS: The U.S. Department of Health and Human Services is a cabinet-level federal department that has the goal of protecting the health of all Americans and providing essential human services.

IPAB: The Independent Payment Advisory Board is a 15-member U.S. government agency created in 2010 by the Patient Protection and Affordable Care Act which has the explicit task of achieving specified savings in Medicare without affecting coverage or quality. IPAB has the authority to make changes to Medicare with Congress being given the power to overrule the agency's decisions through supermajority vote.

MA: The Medicare Advantage program, also known as Medicare Part C, through which beneficiaries can elect to receive Medicare benefits through a private health system.

MACRA: The Medicare Access and CHIP Reauthorization Act, the historic Medicare reform law that repealed the Sustainable Growth Rate (SGR) formula.

Medicaid: The health program for poor Americans, created in 1965, state administered and jointly funded by the federal and state governments.

Medicare: The health program for elderly Americans, created in 1965, and subsequently extended to the disabled and people with end stage renal disease; federally funded and administered. Medicare has four parts: Part A (health facilities), Part B (health professional services), Part C (MA), and Part D (the prescription drug benefit).

PCORI: The Patient-Centered Outcomes Research Institute is a non-governmental institute created as part of a modification to the Social Security Act by clauses in the Patient Protection an Affordable Care Act. It investigates the relative effectiveness of various medical treatments, and Medicare may consider the Institute's research in determining what sorts of therapies it will cover

Single payer: A health system in which the government is financially responsible for providing individuals with health coverage.

Stark: The law that prohibits doctors from making money (with limited exceptions) from certain kinds of healthcare businesses when they make referrals.

Universal coverage: The goal of ensuring that every individual in a health system has some kind of health coverage.

RECAP

Summaries: Highlights/Refresher/Talking Points About This Book

We recognize that From ObamaCare to TrumpCare is dense (as in tightly packed with complex ideas, not as in unintelligent!) and covers a lot of territory. You may not be sure if you are ready to dive in. You may want a refresher. Or you may want to have sound bites ready to impress friends and colleagues. No matter what your motivation, this Appendix includes something for everyone – one-liner summary options, a one-paragraph summary, and a one-page summary of the book.

One-Line Summaries

Looking for a Social Media post on From ObamaCare to TrumpCare? It's tough to get into the details, but try out these options:

U.S. healthcare is broken. From ObamaCare to TrumpCare highlights how the political battles distract from the real problems that need fixing, access and affordability.

Panicked about TrumpCare? Nelson and Fuller offer hope that President Trump will negotiate better deals for the government and patients – not take away people's healthcare.

From ObamaCare to TrumpCare is a call to action to begin the conversation about U.S. healthcare that politicians are afraid to talk about.

Fixing U.S. healthcare boils down to ensuring access and driving affordability. Still a long way to go.

The One-Paragraph Version

U.S. healthcare is broken. The Affordable Care Act (ACA) represented a series of compromises that got the buy-in of stakeholders in the U.S. health system (i.e., drug companies, insurers, and doctors) to fund a series of reforms that would share costs, fill the gaps, and move toward gradual improvement of the system. The ACA broke through the access gap by expanding Medicaid and opening the insurance exchanges. Unfortunately, the failure to contain costs and negative messaging drove its unpopularity, leading to its impending repeal. Following the repeal, Republican energies and Trump's deal-making are likely to result in more price competition from insurers, drug companies, and healthcare providers. Nelson and Fuller offer hope that the new version will improve affordability without taking us backwards on access.

The One (Okay, More Than One!) Page Version

Chapter 1 – Setting the Scene: The Brokenness of U.S. Healthcare

U.S. healthcare is beset by systemic challenges, including (1) relative price; (2) mediocre outcomes; (3) lack of access; and (4) cost allocation. America's health gap reflects insufficient investment in social support, education, diet, and housing – which results in healthcare inequality, substandard care for the poorest Americans, and a pathetic record compared to other countries that spend less and get better outcomes. The U.S. system is lacking in any coherent design, and instead is the product of a patchwork of the 1965 overlay of Medicare and Medicaid coverage, atop the predominant trend of employer-based coverage. The enduring ambivalence about the breadth of the Medicaid program and coverage for poor Americans set the stage for a continuing problem of gaps in access to care and a continuing conundrum about how to rectify the gap.

Chapter 2 - The Strange, Wonkish Road to ObamaCare

Since the 1970s, there have been four decades of failed healthcare reform efforts focused on closing the remaining post-Medicare and post-Medicaid gaps. Amidst the failures of Presidents Nixon and Clinton, in particular, the U.S. has instead had a series of smaller incremental changes addressing particular problems – including expanding Medicare to the disabled, EMTALA for emergency care for the uninsured, and COBRA for the unemployed. The Obama administration broke through and achieved healthcare reform by learning from Clinton-era failures and assembling a compromise that got stakeholder buy-in for the ACA. Rather than a single-payer public option that progressive Democrats (including perhaps Obama himself) have historically wanted, the ACA represented a realistic compromise that actually borrowed from concepts that, once upon a time, were a Republican vision of healthcare: an individual mandate for the uninsured with subsidies, a large employer mandate to strengthen employer coverage, Medicaid expansion for the poorest Americans, and a grab bag of care improvement initiatives. Democrats passed the ACA narrowly on the eve of turning political tides, which were linked to the unpopularity of the ACA.

Chapter 3 - The Good, Bad, and Ugly of ObamaCare Implementation

The ACA's implementation has been a mixed bag, offering triumphs that the half of America who loved the law can embrace, and disasters that the half of America who hated the law can blame. Some of the battle was a legitimate philosophical dispute over the role of government and the limitations of the market and some was empty rhetoric that scared voters. Some was the story of a messy process of working out the kinks in U.S. healthcare. While the Republican messaging won the day in cementing a negative view of the ACA as ruining U.S. healthcare, the reality is that it accomplished a landmark achievement in securing coverage for 20-30 million Americans. (The higher number includes pre-ACA Medicaid expansion during President Obama's presidency.) At the same time, the individual mandate failed to bring young healthy American into the insurance exchanges and the model failed to stabilize or rein in rising healthcare costs. The Supreme Court decisions also set the stage for a very different reality in the Medicaid expansion and hold-out states. The 2016 Republican victory sets America on a course for a new chapter and new direction.

Chapter 4 – A Better Way? The Republican Plan for U.S. Healthcare

The Republican plan for healthcare, encapsulated in House Speaker Paul Ryan's "Better Way" white paper, offers a vision that shares ObamaCare's reform of health insurance underwriting practices, but emphasizes a small government, market-driven approach. The Republican focus on a narrower role for health insurance and more out-of-pocket consumer spending to correct distortions in healthcare pricing holds out some promise. Republicans also champion further privatization of Medicare and extensive deregulation of health insurance and employer coverage. The most divergent aspect of the Republican vision is Medicaid: while they are conservative in disrupting the Medicare program and limiting options for American seniors, their vision would undo the gains achieved by the ACA for the poorest Americans. Although the Republican plan has positive aspects in introducing more market efficiency and consumer-driven behavior, there is no serious effort to deal with the financial costs of care for poor Americans who need chronic care.

Chapter 5 - The Trump Wild Card
Many Democrats and, in particular, people who have gained Medicaid and insurance coverage through the ACA, are terrified of President Trump. Judging from his personal pronouncements on healthcare, however, Donald Trump is actually moderate and departs from Republicans on key issues, including universal coverage and enabling Medicare to negotiate drug prices. While he may not have the interest or desire to get deeply into healthcare, he is unlikely to allow Congressional Republicans to brand his presidency with stripping millions of Americans of their healthcare coverage.

Chapter 6 - Envisioning TrumpCare
When the 115th Congress reconvenes after at least 60 separate repeal votes in the past six years, the vote to repeal the ACA is going to be a potent symbolic moment for Republicans. At the same time, the effective date of the repeal is likely to be put off for at least two years to avoid panic and massive disruption, leaving intact most people's coverage for the time being. Meanwhile, if President Trump and Congressional Republicans can reach agreement, they will have to move more quickly on other aspects of their agenda, such as expanding opportunities for health savings accounts, deregulating insurance at the state level, and doing away with projects that Republicans can't stand (e.g., PCORI, IPAB, and CMMI). The end result may end up being little forward movement beyond a number of symbolic victories for President Trump and Speaker Ryan. The big questions ahead in the near term are whether President Trump and Congressional Republicans are going to choose ideological purity or popularity, because they can't have

both. Republican tax reform presents a very different and much harsher financial exposure to healthcare expenses for most Americans.

Chapter 7 - This is Real: Implications for Patients

How will TrumpCare affect patients across the spectrum? The challenge has always been that, for different patients, the implications are very different. For a poor patient receiving Medicaid as a result of President Obama and people who otherwise would be without coverage, the overriding issue has been fear that the gains of the past seven years will be undone. This fear may be overstated given the reluctance of President Trump (and potentially Republicans) to impose an ideologically pure solution at the cost of incurring voter wrath. Nonetheless, significant changes are coming that are going to impose a much higher financial burden on individuals if the Republican tax reform approach to healthcare passes. States are expected to blunt the impact both by forthcoming litigation from Democratic state attorney generals challenging any changes, as well as by efforts in certain states to solidify resources. The challenge is that, for people living in ObamaCare/Medicaid expansion hold-out states, the situation is already much worse and the disparities are only widening.

Chapter 8 - Unprepared? Implications for the Healthcare Industry

The impact of legislative changes on the different segments of the healthcare industry are significant. Hospitals are bracing to be big losers under TrumpCare, having given up funding sources and now facing the prospect of absorbing more uninsured care. For physicians, TrumpCare may cozy up to physician interests, but ultimately won't change the status quo. The post-acute sector (skilled nursing facilities and home health agencies) appear to have dodged a bullet if Republicans suspend the bundled payment initiatives as they are threatening to do. Providers of women's health and family planning are in for a grim period of defunding and legal challenges. The marijuana industry is bracing for a rollback under Attorney General Sessions. Meanwhile, life science providers will benefit from some regulatory loosening, but are nervous that they may bear the brunt of President Trump's acidic Twitter account over pricing and the bad deal that doesn't allow Medicare to negotiate drug prices. The insurance companies are celebrating a presidency that puts them in the driver's seat in U.S. healthcare.

Chapter 9 - How TrumpCare Intersects with Broader Forces of Healthcare Transformation

For all of the tension over how the political conflict around the repeal and the Republican alternative plays out, some of the legislative shifts are muted by broader economic, behavioral, and technological changes that are transforming healthcare. Healthcare has been undergoing a massive transformation as it adapts to the new expectations and demands of a consumerist, underinsured, and aging population. Technology has been driving incredible breakthroughs that will improve quality and reduce cost in healthcare. At the same time, the elephant in the room that politicians are not talking about is the impact of technology, machine learning, and robotics in eliminating not just industrial jobs, but, increasingly, middle management and a wide range of professional services, raising the structural rate of unemployment and reshaping the healthcare needs of the future. Realignment, consolidation, and the emergence of a new competitive landscape with competition from retail and other sectors is also remaking the industry. All of these factors are much larger long-term determinants of the future of healthcare than the change in government policy from the Obama and Trump presidencies.

Chapter 10 - Big Questions Ahead: Where Do We Go From Here?

While there are good reasons not to panic about the impact of the ACA repeal, there are bigger reasons to despair about things like compromise-killing political polarization, the unlikelihood of consensus on universal coverage as a goal, and the inability of our political leaders to be able to talk, let alone compromise, on the real challenges in fixing U.S. healthcare: access and affordability. In the absence of political leadership, we issue a call to action: Americans need to begin honest, open conversations about the challenges in fixing healthcare that no one wants to talk about with people of opposing perspectives. Can the current polarization be broken? Looking towards 2020/2024, we look to the death of the ACA to lead Democrats to coalesce, after some soul searching, around a vision of Americanized single-payer. While politically viable options are in short supply, we offer some thoughts about what solutions should look like to fix the brokenness of U.S. healthcare. We need to move beyond our half-century of ambivalence for providing care to people who can't afford it and towards a solution that ensures universal access to core healthcare needs for all Americans. We see a smaller role for insurance, to cover catastrophic events and pharmaceuticals, leaving Americans the choice to buy broader elective insurance or pay out-of-pocket for more healthcare expenses. These aren't the only options, but we need to start experimenting, because what we're doing now isn't working.

INDEX

END NOTES

[1] State of Illinois, Department of Public Health, Chronic Disease Burden Update, Volume 2, Issue 18 (November 2013).

[2] Kaiser Family Foundation, http://kff.org/medicare/fact-sheet/medicare-spending-and-financing-fact-sheet/

[3] Kaiser Family Foundation, http://kff.org/medicaid/state-indicator/federalstate-share-of-spending/

[4] Donald Trump, Dallas, September 14, 2015. This and other quotes attributable to Trump are drawn from Beckers Hospital Review ("8 Donald Trump quotes on healthcare," Mary Rechtoris, August 16, 2016) and also dated based on specific news reports.

[5] CNN, http://www.cnn.com/2016/10/25/politics/trump-obamacare-employees/

[6] Washington Examiner, http://www.washingtonexaminer.com/trump-flip-flops-on-obamacare-mandate-in-less-than-24-hours/article/2583703

[7] Washington Post, https://www.washingtonpost.com/news/post-politics/wp/2015/08/06/annotated-transcript-the-aug-6-gop-debate/?utm_term=.20fc6b0e0071

[8] STAT, https://www.statnews.com/2016/01/26/trump-negotiate-drug-prices/

[9] CBS News, http://www.cbsnews.com/news/60-minutes-donald-trump-family-melania-ivanka-lesley-stahl/

[10] Kaiser Health News, http://khn.org/morning-breakout/trump-says-aca-will-destroy-health-care-in-america-promises-special-session-to-repeal-it/

[11] MSNBC, http://www.msnbc.com/msnbc-quick-cuts/watch/trump-i-won-t-let-people-die-in-the-streets-631593027801.

[12] Washington Post, https://www.washingtonpost.com/news/the-fix/wp/2016/04/03/donald-trumps-ever-shifting-positions-on-abortion/?utm_term=.278fea2f6243

[13] Time, http://time.com/4591183/time-person-of-the-year-2016-donald-trump-interview/

[14] Kaiser Health News, http://khn.org/news/medicaid-coverage-for-addiction-treatment-varies-dramatically/

[15] OnTheIssues.org (quoting ABC This Week 2015 interview by Martha Raddatz, Nov 8, 2015).

[16] OnTheIssues.org (quoting Source: Washington Post 2015 coverage of 2016 presidential hopefuls, Oct 29, 2015).

[17] Kaiser Health News, http://khn.org/morning-breakout/senates-to-do-list-for-day-one-repeal-health-law/